THE
SLIM
GOURMET

by Martin Lederman

SIMON AND SCHUSTER

New York, 1955

First Printing

LIBRARY OF CONGRESS CATALOG CARD NUMBER: 55-5942 ..
DEWEY DECIMAL CLASSIFICATION NUMBER: 641.01
MANUFACTURED IN THE UNITED STATES OF AMERICA
BY H. WOLFF BOOK MFG. CO., INC., NEW YORK
DESIGNED BY BETTY KORMUSIS

TO GABRIELE
this book is dedicated
as is its author.

ACKNOWLEDGMENTS

WHAT *author does not believe that every thought and phrase of his book are his and his alone, especially when it has taken years to develop and test what seems a new way of looking at old things?*

This writer is different. Without the contributions of hundreds of authorities in many fields to our eating lore—cooks and scientists, waiters and wine tasters, doctors and philosophers— this book could never have been written.

My obligation to so many precludes a recital of names. Let me mention only Brillat-Savarin among the Slim Gourmet's numerous ancestors.

I am grateful for the encouragement and co-operation of my wife, and for the lively interest of Nina and Harry Abrams in the Slim Gourmet and his problems.

Ruth Goode's suggestions and loving care in preparing the manuscript were invaluable.

My thanks also to the thousands who wrote me in response to my articles in a number of leading American newspapers, and to the many others who have told me of the success with which they have adopted the Slim Gourmet's way in their lives.

MARTIN LEDERMAN

New York
February, 1955

Contents

Book Two: THE SLIM GOURMET'S WAY TO REDUCE

Step by Step through a Tested Technique of Losing Weight Without Dieting, Without Sacrifice, With More Enjoyment and for Good

Book Three: THE JOY OF EATING

Slim Gourmet Experiences and Discoveries With Many Foods at Home and Abroad, at Drugstore Counters and in Fine Restaurants

Book One

THE SLIM GOURMET'S

PHILOSOPHY

1 TWENTY-FIVE YEARS

AND SEVENTEEN DIETS

I have been interested in food all my life. I am an avid reader of menu cards, cookbooks, books on wine and books on nutrition, books on meat carving and books on distilling, books on serving and books on gastronomy. But dearer to me than books is the practice of the art of eating. This sweet practice I have exercised under many skies. I know the taste of oysters in Massachusetts and snails in Burgundy, of a steak in Chicago and a trout broiled an hour after it was caught in a Swiss mountain brook.

For a long time I gave so much attention to the enjoyment of food and drink that I forgot to look at my waistline. When I finally saw that I must take reducing seriously, I turned from the wonderful world of foods to the nutritional sciences that teach us how to eat for health and longer life.

I found to my surprise that the food experts are divided into two camps. From one camp, the lovers of food and eating, guardians of the traditions of great cuisines, tempt us with cookbooks and recipes to refine and cultivate our tastes. From the other camp, whose beginnings go back only about fifty years, the nutritionists, dietitians, and students of body chemistry urge upon us nutritional patterns which theoretically satisfy the body's needs. These bitter opponents battle for our souls. The gourmets make our mouths water and our waistlines grow, and the nutritionists take the joy out of eating.

To which camp do you belong? To which camp do I belong? To which philosophy should one subscribe? I was at a loss. Meanwhile something had to be done. And so I began to diet.

My dieting success was like that of my friend S. This distinguished French journalist invited twelve friends to a fabulous dinner party in one of the great eating places of Paris. It was his "eve of a diet" dinner party; he gave it regularly once a year and for three successive years I was present. The following morning he went on a diet: For breakfast, an apple; for lunch, one lamb chop and two tablespoons of spinach; for dinner, raw carrot, plain omelet, and salad without dressing. Instead of his customary choice wines he drank only water. Whoever knows water in Paris will understand his sacrifice. After four or six weeks S. had lost ten or fifteen pounds. He advertised it to everyone and we all congratulated him on his achievement. A few weeks later, without advertising, anyone could see that he had gained back every ounce.

Who has not had a similar experience?

I have had seventeen of them, in many countries and various languages.

Dix-sept, siebzehn, diciasette, diez y siete, SEVENTEEN separate and distinct diets failed, deceived, and disappointed me although I followed them faithfully. With the eighteenth—which was no diet at all but the Slim Gourmet's philosophy—I lost eighty pounds and have since remained, without pain, without sacrifice, at the 168 pounds my doctor and I like better.

During my twenty-five years of dieting I starved and worried and harried away more than four hundred pounds. Each time I regained what I had grimly struggled to lose, and within weeks or at best a few months after the end of each diet I was searching for a new and different one.

Nearly the first and probably the worst was the Marienbad cure. This was popular in Europe between 1880 and 1930; I was a victim in 1930. I paid the learned doctors of this world-renowned health spa to starve me in the midst of some of the finest cooking in the world; the juiciest boiled hams, the finest rolls, the most titillating desserts, were prepared and consumed in the hotels and restaurants of Marienbad, right under my nose. But the unresisting patient was purged three times a day, ordered to perform strenuous exercises, and melted in Turkish baths, and in three weeks he emerged a reduced mental wreck.

I left Marienbad in August. By Christmas I had regained both my equilibrium and my weight.

A year or two later I was in Paris, enjoying among other pleasures the performance of Pauley, that French comedian famous for his spirited jibes at his country's politics. Two days later, over my breakfast brioche, I read that Pauley had died of a heart attack. He weighed 270 pounds, and when I stepped on the scale the needle swung almost to the same figure. The following week, my business in Paris hastily concluded, I was already in Brides-les-Bains, a resort in the Haute Savoie, taking the Marienbad cure with French trimmings.

This time I lost twenty pounds in three weeks. This time, too, I was determined to accomplish my purpose once and for all. When I left Brides-les-Bains I carried with me the recommendations of its doctors. For six gruesome months I continued to lose at the rate of ten pounds a month.

In Paris that March I met Dr. X of Brides-les-Bains. He did not recognize me at first and when I identified myself he appeared rather shaken. He invited me to lunch.

At lunch he pressed upon me the very dishes that in his official capacity he had severely forbidden me. He said genially, "We never expect a patient to follow our instructions. The usual thing is to come back to Brides and take the cure again the following summer. Many of our patients are regular visitors. Madame de Y. has been coming every summer for fifteen years."

It was my turn to be shaken. These doctors themselves did not believe in their diets!

I left the luncheon table feeling well fed but also rather foolish at having taken the good doctor's prescription so seriously. Apparently he had never considered the possibility that reducing could be a one-time job with permanent results. With his implied blessing I relaxed, went back to my pleasant ways—and gained back the sixty pounds I had labored so hard to lose.

There followed in order through the years: the Hollywood diet, the one-food-each-day-a-week diet, the bread-and-butter diet, the steak-three-times-a-day, straight-way-to-bankruptcy diet, the sweet-before-each-meal diet, the two-meals-a-day diet, the only-reducing-foods diet, the ABC diet, the eighteen-day diet, and many more that it would pain both the reader and myself to recall. Some were alluring, some revolting; I wrestled with them all. Whenever I learned of a new way to reduce quickly, I followed the advice, whether it was printed or spoken on phonograph records, whether it meant saying good-by to bread or sweets or drinks or big portions or between-meal snacks or butter or cream. I dieted on 1,200 calories and I dieted on 1,000 calories and I dieted on 800 calories. But invariably I gained back in a few months what I had lost in a few months, until I got tired of this escalator dieting.

For the next three years I did not diet at all. I was fed up, weary, cynical, and not in the least amused. I was also, once more, hopelessly overweight.

I began to observe my own ways of eating. And I made a remarkable discovery. I had always been under the impression that I was overeating very heavily. When I took inventory of my actual eating, I found that I was not overeating *heavily*. I was eating only one or two hundred calories a day too much!

Now it is not dangerous to eat one or two hundred extra calories a day for a day or two. But the year has 365 days, and only 100 surplus calories a day through the year add up to ten pounds of overweight. All because of one extra roll every day!

It had taken me four or five years to assemble my overweight in this way. By leaving out that one extra roll I might have kept my weight steady. By doing without another roll or its equivalent of 100 calories each day I might even have lost, over four or five years, the overweight I had gained.

Had I ever given thought to the matter in this way? Of course not. I had only wanted to get rid of the fat I had patiently gathered over so many years and I wanted to get rid of it as fast as possible.

This is the way most of us feel about our overweight. This is the frame of mind in which we become easy prey to logical or illogical, scientific or unscientific diet fads. We accept the most rigorous regime, deny ourselves our favorite foods and most innocent table pleasures. We go to bed without a snack and to work without breakfast. We talk ourselves into the self-centered watchfulness of a person who is dangerously ill. We lose two pounds, three pounds, four pounds a week and are naïvely proud of our feat.

I think it is heroic, this way of dieting, but how long can a normal human being be a hero?

I still remember many after-diet first meals. They were not excessive. I did not go directly from one lamb chop to breaded cutlet and French-fried potatoes and goose liver pâté and unlimited drinks. My longing was not to eat a great deal but to taste things again. To taste bread again—to taste wine again—to have again the wonderful feeling of having spent an hour at the table and dined well. For wanting to satisfy such harmless, normal desires, we who have dieted can hardly be accused of lacking will power!

Most of the so-called wonder diets are medically and nutritionally correct and can be followed comfortably enough under hospital conditions. The trouble comes when we apply them to our day-to-day living, eating at the family table, working in offices and factories, following the familiar habits and tastes and eating ways of our normal environment. Man does not eat for calories alone! Mealtime is a time for relaxation, for companionship, for communication with our fellow human beings. Mealtime is also a time for the enjoyment of food itself.

The diets ignore all this. They leave us our tensions, the pressures of our day, our longing for the shared pleasures that mealtime has stood for through the ages—and make of eating a grim, dour self-punishment. If we submit we become miserable, if not actually neurotic. If we rebel—and most of us, being basically healthy, do rebel—we are condemned forever to being overweight. They offer us no other alternative.

Are we really gluttons, as the diets imply we are? I have found no evidence of it. I have studied not only my own eating, but the eating habits of thousands of American men and women from Coast to Coast. I have very rarely found one who eats more than ten per cent in excess of what his daily calories should be.

Meanwhile each diet leaves its scars. Each has its own slant, its own list of forbidden foods. Beer is fattening. So is butter, so is bread, so are chocolate and ice cream. Countless people never dare to enjoy a banana or a potato. Countless good and innocent foods have had their reputations blasted for all time by the libelous accusation, "Fattening!"

Long after the diet has been forgotten and the slim waist has thickened again, we continue to be ruled by the diet's narrow food vocabulary. Not content with taking the fun out of eating during the diet, the diet designers take the fun out of eating for the rest of our lives. A well-known woman writer, who in the course of five years had gone through five revolutionary wonder diets, now retains one or two ideas from each. From one almost forgotten food fad she remembers never to mix carbohydrates and proteins at the same meal. According to another she spends one day a week in bed, taking no food and only four glasses of skimmed milk. Every morning she downs two tablespoons of blackstrap molasses, a vestige of still another diet. Despite long working hours and a tense nervous temperament she allows herself no more than three meals a day, with never a comforting or relaxing snack between meals or before bed.

By her own confession she is an unhappy woman who "hates food," dislikes her table companions, makes astonishing slips in table conversation, and tries endlessly to regain her mental balance on the couches of psychoanalysts.

Food and eating are bound up with our deepest emotions. We first know love when as infants we are fed; we first experience anxiety when food is withheld. We eat in celebration and in mourning, and to allay our worry when the outcome of an event is in doubt. We eat joyfully with our loved ones and we also eat when we feel unloved. To maintain our emotional stability in a challenging world is hard enough. Yet we carelessly taint with anxiety and guilt the very food that sustains us!

Food has been a potent magic since the dawn of man. In his classic *The Golden Bough* Frazer writes of "Taboos on Leaving Food Over." Primitive men carefully bury the unfinished scrap of meat or the peel of a banana. If an enemy were to find the scrap and burn it, the one who had eaten of it would sicken and die unless he hastily sent gifts to persuade the disease-maker that he should stop burning the banana peel.

For primitive man the very laws of hospitality were based on the magic of food. If I entertain you at dinner, you and I have a physical bond because the same food is in our stomachs. Whatever harms you will surely harm me as well. I therefore will take the greatest care of you, my guest. Not only will I myself do you no injury, but I will also give you every protection while you are under my roof and see you safely on your way when you depart.

Food is the magic of primitive man and the ethics of civilized man. We offer food and drink to each other out of a human wish to be close, to share pleasure and well-being, to nurture friendship and cultivate the art of civilized living. We give food to the hungry as we hope it will be given to us. We carry food to the sick and offer food to the grieving. And we do not look for honor or even simple honesty in a man who is starving.

All this the wonder diets ignore. All this they brush aside as though the staff of life, the foundation of our emotional stability and shared humanity, were simply so many calories.

When I began to understand the real meaning of food I was shocked at the diet designers for tampering with it so lightly.

I was even more shocked at myself for following them so blindly.

A word deserves to be said here in defense of doctors, who also on occasion give us printed diets for our health's sake. One cannot go to a doctor and expect him in the course of a short visit to do the job a psychiatrist takes two or three years to accomplish. The doctor knows the facts of his patient's body, and the facts of medicine and biology, but out of these facts he cannot *create normality*. The pattern of normality is individual with each of us. No doctor can design it for the patient out of a single visit, or even occasional or periodic visits.

Any diet, however disagreeable, may be good for four or eight weeks. But it is a rare person who can spend the rest of his life going contrary to his very nature. Sooner or later he asks himself, why should he do this violence to himself? Does the end really justify these means? What is so wrong with the pleasant ways, the comfortable ways of the past?

And so, having lost x pounds but learned nothing in the course of it except that dieting is a torture he will be obliged to undergo again and again, he returns to the world of the living and enjoys his reprieve from the diet prison by again eating unwisely and too well.

So it was with me for twenty-five years and seventeen diets, until, with myself as my own best subject for study, I set out on my search for a new food philosophy.

2 THE TWENTIETH-CENTURY WAY

Why does twentieth-century man need a new food philosophy? We are not different physically from the Greeks who applauded Sophocles' plays, or the Romans in their togas who made speeches in the Forum. Our bodies require the same proteins and starches, the same minerals and vitamins as did theirs. We may eat more beef and less lamb than Jacob and his brethren, less venison and more domesticated meat than Robin Hood. We have developed many fruits and vegetables that did not appear even on Marie Antoinette's table. But we still eat bread and meat, vegetables and fruits. The day when we take our nourishment in capsules rather than in delicious-tasting dishes is still, we hope, far in the future. We can still, like Henry VIII, enjoy a real drumstick from a real chicken, though we no longer consider it good manners to throw the bone on the dining room floor.

Yet there have been changes that affect our eating in a thousand ways. We only need to mention two friends of twentieth-century man, so familiar that we take their kind services for granted every day of our lives: the gasoline motor and the electric outlet.

In the old days only royalty and aristocrats rode on horses or elephants or in sedan chairs; others walked. The automobile has made of Americans a nation of non-walkers. In our houses we do not climb stairs but ride in elevators (or build our suburban homes on the ground level). The housewife does not beat the rugs out-of-doors or the family laundry at the river bank. She rarely even beats an egg.

Goethe and Benjamin Franklin stood at their desks to write. Today, everybody sits! The farmer who once swung his scythe to harvest his grain now sits riding a harvester. The construction worker who swung pick and shovel sits on a bulldozer. All of

these, including the mother of a family, still use more muscle—
and more calories—than the man who sits at a desk while his
brain does the work. But they use perhaps 300 fewer calories
each day than their grandfathers and grandmothers, to do the
same work. Do they—or any of us in this motorized age—
habitually eat that much less?

I doubt that we do. I think rather that most of us in this part
of the world eat more than most of the men and women of a
century ago. We have more to eat and more time to eat it. A
hundred years ago most people worked seventy hours a week.
Today the average American works forty hours—a bonus of
thirty hours each week to rest, to play, and to eat and drink.

To overeat and grow fat was formerly the privilege only of the
aristocrat and the rich man. Ordinary men could afford only a
lean diet, and not more than enough to keep them alive. In ancient China a mandarin was recognized as much by his girth as
by his rich clothes. Even today some Eastern peoples—the Arabs
for example—measure a man's wealth by his stoutness or the
stoutness of his wives. But today, in the United States at least,
one may have a quite modest bank account and yet be obliged
to reduce.

Human beings, like the animals, were once dependent on the
seasons and the bounty of nature for their food. They ate well
at harvest time, but they were fortunate if the harvest was good
enough to provide food for the winter—and if freeze or thaw or
flood or fire did not destroy their food in storage before the next
harvest. The race memory, they say, lives in all of us. Today in
the United States we have plenty and variety all the year round,
thanks to electricity and the gasoline motor and our highly developed ways of storing food. But too many of us still eat each
meal as though we could not be sure when we would eat the
next!

Above all, we have changed in our attitudes toward the human waistline. In Victorian times fat was the fashion. Queen
Victoria had a comfortable roundness, and her son, King Ed-

ward VII, was a stout gourmet. Teddy Roosevelt filled the Presidential chair well, and William Howard Taft overflowed it. In a nineteenth-century portrait gallery we observe that many Presidents and their ladies were of ample size. (The Fathers of the American Revolution were, on the contrary, rather thinner.) Diamond Jim Brady's menus are legendary, and Lillian Russell was beautiful but not slender. Doctors began frowning upon overweight only after the First World War. With the flapper of the 1920's, fashion, for its own mysterious reasons, began to extol the boyish figure in ladies at about the same time.

Today we look upon fat as unlovely, unhealthy and unfashionable. And so, while we have more for everyone to eat and more time to eat it, we need less food to sustain us. We are also less pleased, indeed we are strongly displeased, to be fat. At the same time we are like our happy, sensible ancestors in wishing to enjoy the pleasures of eating.

This is our dilemma. This is why 26,000,000 Americans are overweight. This is why, in the twentieth century, we need a new food philosophy.

Fortunately, the same progress that has given us this problem can help us to solve it. The electric current that stores our food unspoiled in its natural state or quick-freezes it at its peak of ripeness and flavor, the refrigerated trucks and trains that bring us foods from all parts of the country no matter where we live— green vegetables and citrus fruits in winter, fish from waters a thousand miles away—these will help us to form our new philosophy of eating.

Plenty and variety are keys to this new philosophy. The enjoyment of food, of taste, of natural flavor, are keys to it. The recognition—not the denial—of our own personal and individual ways of eating and enjoying food is a key to it.

Not by denying ourselves the pleasures of food, but by taking still greater joy in our eating, will we become slender and stay slender, says the Slim Gourmet.

First in the Slim Gourmet's philosophy comes *enjoyment* of

eating. When you enjoy your food you eat less. A paradox? If you observe yourself and others, you will see that it is true.

When, in my discontent with my waistline and my despair with diets, I began to watch how I actually ate, I discovered this great truth: at those times when I was inattentive to what I ate, I ate too much. But when a new food, a new *taste*, was before me, I ate slowly, enjoying each mouthful, like a child dawdling over his ice cream to make it last—and I did not need a second helping. With a too-familiar dish I had so little satisfaction of taste that I ate more and yet more, seeking satisfaction. But when I enjoyed the conscious, human satisfaction of *taste*, I did not seek the unconscious, animal satisfaction of stuffing myself full.

If you do not believe this, test yourself. You will find as I did that boredom makes gluttons of us all. We eat because our bodies need nourishment; of this the nutritionists never tire of reminding us. But we also eat for the satisfaction of our taste buds, for the pleasure of our palates. Why else do we have these? If we ate only to replenish our bodies, simple animal hunger would be enough to make us seek the table at certain hours of the day. Probably we would also eat only so much—enough to fuel the cells—and no more. But we seek something else when we eat. We seek satisfaction of our appetite for pleasure as well as for nourishment. And when we satisfy that appetite, we do not eat another and another helping out of frustrated seeking.

Americans do not know how good their tastes are, and how wonderfully a bountiful nature and a superb storing and distributing system can satisfy their tastes. Americans have an inferiority feeling about their eating habits. They are ashamed because they do not cook with sauces or rave over a ragout. They are on the way to greatness in eating when they prefer a steak to a goulash and a grapefruit to a fruitcake. Americans like their food simple, *natural*. They eat food as it grows, with little more than the application of heat to make it edible: their beef broiled, their birds roasted, their peas and stringbeans cooked simply in salted water and served with butter.

If Americans were to follow their natural tastes in food, and at the same time make use of the plenty and variety that is theirs in the nearest supermarket, they would have the greatest enjoyment of eating of any people in the world—*and they would never be overweight!* The greatest dangers to the American waistline are boredom, monotony, familiarity in food, all of which lead to overeating, and a hesitancy about cultivating the pleasure of taste.

The supermarket is the twentieth century's creative contribution to our food philosophy. Behind it is a distribution system whose complexities we can scarcely begin to imagine and do not need to probe. All we need to do is look at the shelves and bins and refrigerator cases, as rich in color, composition, and suggested harmony as a gallery of paintings. But do we look? Alas, we go up and down the aisles, looking only at the shopping list in our hand, picking from shelf and bin and case only this item and that item that we ate yesterday and are lacking today. The variety, the interest, the novelty, of the neighboring items are lost to our unseeing eye as we bend quickly again to the same monotonous shopping list.

When you go to France or Italy or England, you conscientiously make a tour of the art galleries and the cathedrals, perhaps also of the markets like the famous ones in Paris and Marseille. Once, only once, go like a tourist to your supermarket. Go at a time when it is not crowded. Carry a notebook and pencil, and go slowly down and up the aisles, looking at everything as you go. Stop for example at the cheese case, where you habitually reach for a half pound of Swiss or American. This time look at the thirty or forty different kinds of cheeses there. (In a suburban supermarket I once counted forty-seven; in a Midwestern department-store grocery shop there were sixty-eight.) Instead of the half pound of your usual cheese, this time try a quarter pound or so of two or three. And write in your notebook the names of others that look interesting, to sample the next time.

Do the same with the vegetable bins, the meat cases. Look at the noodles and the spaghetti. Nowhere in the world is there such inspiration for variety and novelty to add to the joy of eating and the encouragement of slimness, as in the American supermarket. Never in history has variety been so easy to achieve.

Time was when the seasons themselves forced man to eat in variety. If oranges were not in season he could not eat them; he had to eat cherries, or strawberries, or whatever fruit was available. Even potatoes were not to be had all the year round, and people filled in with noodles, dried beans, rice, and other cereals. Today if you want to think only of orange juice for breakfast, and potatoes with your meat at dinner, they are there for you to have, at the risk of monotony in your diet and enlargement of your girth. The choice, however, is yours; you can have tangerine juice or pineapple juice or a dish of blueberries for breakfast, and a dozen substitutes for potatoes at your dinner.

The final, perhaps the most important, point in the Slim Gourmet's philosophy is individuality. We talk a great deal about the individual in the twentieth century, about his rights and his responsibilities and his privileges. The French and the American Revolutions were made for the sake of individual freedom. Yet in eating—and especially in dieting for slimness—the individual is largely ignored. Each wonder diet prescribes for all.

Eating is a most personal experience. We each have personal likes and dislikes in food, personal associations with this or that food. Some of us eat well in the morning, some not until dinner, some like a hearty lunch. Some can never eat between meals or before bed, some are not happy unless they do. All this individuality of likes and needs the diets brush aside as unimportant self-indulgence.

The Slim Gourmet disagrees vigorously. The individuality of eating is one of the reasons why diets fail. The individuality of eating is what will help everyone to become slim while eating with pleasure. It is only by knowing how he actually eats and how he likes to eat that each individual can shake off, once and for all, his extra pounds, and live at peace with himself and his normal weight.

Most people do not seriously overeat. Yet they can, and many do, become seriously overweight. The extra pounds can come only from extra calories, but they come from only a few extra calories—100 or 200—a day. Each person has his own way of taking in these extra calories.

Is it the beer he drinks while watching television? Must he give up the beer? Not at all. There are ways to drink less beer with the same pleasure and comfort, as we shall see, and perhaps he can also easily cut some calories, which he will never miss, from another meal, to leave part of his calorie budget for the beer that he so enjoys.

Is it the midnight snack? And if so, must he give up this pleasant and often beneficial little extra repast? The bite at bedtime helps many people to sleep better than they otherwise would. Doctors actually recommend it to a number of their patients. It can be as effective for some as a sleeping pill, and surely it is more wholesome. For many people—and I am one of them—the bite at bedtime makes this a cherished time of day. It quiets the day's tensions, puts a gentle period to the day's stimulating challenges. It provides a moment of philosophy, of meditation, of quiet conversation with wife or husband, of summing up the day's living and putting one's emotional household in order. For those of us to whom it has such values, no diet that forbids the midnight snack can succeed. We may give up the comfort of a bite at bedtime for the few weeks of the diet, but we have too much sense— or our personal needs are too demanding—to give it up permanently. And so the few extra calories begin adding up again to the extra pounds that we do not want.

But it is simple enough, once you know what your midnight

snack means to you, to save those calories from another part of the day, and have your comfort at bedtime without paying for it in overweight.

For one person the surplus is no more than an extra slice of buttered toast at breakfast, or two eggs when he could do with one. For another it is a lunch which makes him feel stuffed and heavy all afternoon, and which, if he thinks about it a moment, he can easily modify.

Why we overeat is also a very personal matter. Each has his own good reasons for what he does. In everyone's life there are tensions and pressures; some of us find that we eat more when we are tense, when we are anxious. Nervous eating is an insidious accumulator of weight; it is the kind of eating of which we are usually not even aware. The bowl of potato chips or peanuts empties before us, and we are not conscious that we have stretched out our hands more than once or twice.

We cannot make the nerves and the tension vanish by a magic spell. We cannot eliminate the nervous eating that often gives us comfort under tension, without increasing the nervousness and the tension. If our need for peanuts at that moment is strong enough, it is probable that we will eat them anyway, and be guilty afterward as well as overweight. We cannot rely on a law that will forbid us to indulge in nervous eating. We need a technique for getting the comfort of eating when we need it, and yet protecting ourselves from the penalty of overweight.

Our bodies all need substantially the same elements of nutrition, but no two individuals need to take these elements in the same way. Each has his own pattern. For each individual his own eating personality is his own best guide to the comfort and health of a normal weight combined with the joy of eating.

This is the Slim Gourmet's philosophy for eating in the twentieth century. We will see now how to put it into practice.

3 TASTE IS THE KEY

TO JOY AND SLIMNESS

Can your tongue distinguish between a lemon and a slice of Virginia ham? Then you have taste!

But perhaps you cannot tell the difference between Roquefort cheese and Gorgonzola. Then you have taste but not experience. Or you do not astound the dinner guests by guessing from a sip the year in which the wine was grown and the region. Then you are an honest citizen without pretense.

There are those who try to impress us with a refinement they may or may not have. And there are others who boast, "I have no sense of taste. I don't know what I'm eating!" Both attitudes are open to question. I am inclined to think that neither the show-off with the wine waiter nor the man who will eat anything "just so it is food!" is quite honest with himself or with others. Every one of us, man, woman, and child, is endowed with taste and the freedom to neglect or cultivate it. Brillat-Savarin called his book, published in 1825, *The Physiology of Taste,* and in his famous first two "meditations" he described biologically and anatomically the functioning of our senses and the mechanics of taste. This eminent judge and discriminating eater became so enthusiastic about the facts of biology that he quite forgot to tell us how to cultivate, improve, and refine one's taste, which was surely his original intention.

It may be informative and even entertaining to know all there is to know about the palate and the interaction of taste buds, tongue, and saliva. But the Slim Gourmet is more interested in knowing how one can develop this mysterious faculty of taste and put it to service. For he sees in taste a key to the joy of eating, and a tool for becoming and remaining slim. Taste, the pleasure of food, saves us from the automatic overeating that is responsible for so much of our overweight.

Taste is a handmaiden to the enjoyment that will keep us slim. If we eat a frankfurter for its taste, with conscious pleasure, we know we have eaten a frankfurter and are satisfied. But if we do not consciously enjoy the first, we eat another and another, until we are stuffed.

Let us therefore leave biology to the biologists and physiology to the physiologists. Let us talk instead about eating, and how taste can help us to eat for more pleasure, better health, and less weight.

However undeveloped our tastes may be, we have all made some progress in taste refinement since our baby days. Experience has taught us that there are certain distinct eating sensations, which we might classify as: Savor, Flavor, Aroma, and Food feel.

Savor is what our tongue can distinguish. It knows what is sweet or salty, bitter or sour.

Flavor is recognized by the tongue and nose in co-operation. The flavor of a strawberry is different from that of a pineapple, although both are sweet and tart.

Aroma is appreciated by our sense of smell unaided. Remember the aroma of steak broiling on a charcoal fire? Of a bowl of steaming lentil soup on a cold day? Of coffee freshly brewed?

Food feel is registered by tongue and palate. Together these members of the taste family report whether our food is hot or cold, rough or smooth, dry or juicy, acid or mellow, soft or crisp or delicate or crude.

This list is elementary and far from complete, and yet it gives us enough evidence to explode the widely held belief that taste is an experience of the privileged few and unknown to ordinary mortals.

The sense of taste is universal and only an occasional individual is actually lacking in one or another taste sensation. What is true, however, is that the majority of people give little attention to their sense of taste. Most people ignore all but the most striking taste experiences that come their way, pleasant or unpleasant, and some of us notice only the unpleasant ones.

A few people cherish their sense of taste, enjoy it, develop it, improve and refine it. And very few people indeed know that they can use this precious gift of nature to reduce with pleasure and thus to prolong the span of an agreeable life.

Am I suggesting that even the most manly member of the armed forces, like my friend Colonel S. of the United States Army is endowed with a sense of taste, even though before his first bite he covers his omelet with salt and pepper and a noble helping of bottled ketchup, whether he is in Thule or Paris, Atlanta or Tokyo?

I am suggesting precisely that. Colonel S. is unfortunately not a rare case. The violence that he does to his sense of taste is almost unknown among women. They are not ashamed to appreciate food, to distinguish one flavor from another, to taste before seasoning. There are self-conscious men who think it unmanly to devote care and attention to eating. But even a monkey chooses his meal according to his taste. Chimpanzees are known to be gourmets, with a highly individual predilection for certain foods. It is a poor claim to manhood that rests on one's brutality to his taste buds.

Social critics, who probably themselves never enjoyed a good dinner, have pointed to the cultivation of taste as a sign of decaying civilization. They have warned us that Rome fell under the weight of the costly luxuries which burdened Lucullus' table, the Colchester oysters and the peacocks' tongues. Pliny, the tabloid reporter of that day, made headlines of the eating clowneries of some newly rich millionaires, and his sensational stories have persisted through twenty centuries. The many Romans who dined more modestly and more wholesomely would have made dull copy, and so would the countless plebeians who, perhaps, got very little dinner at all and whose hunger very likely had more to do with Rome's decline than the overeating of Lucullus and his guests. Lucullan excesses occur at all times and in all climes.

Refined taste can be found in primitive as well as in civilized society, in humble dwellings as in palaces. It can be found in Turkey, where even the poor are water gourmets who discuss the taste and purity of ordinary drinking water bottled in one town, and compare it with water brought from another town. (New Yorkers or Chicagoans do not know how water can "taste" unless they travel to Vienna or to Alexandria, Egypt, where water is a real delicacy with different varieties to be bought and savored.)

We discover refined taste applied to bread in France, where a child can judge the quality of a loaf according to freshness, crispness, and the skill of the baker.

We find it in Chester County, Pennsylvania, where even manly lawyers are not afraid to confess that they can distinguish between firm good mushrooms and mushy bad ones and don't blush to recommend the restaurant which serves the best stuffed mushrooms in town.

The sense of taste can be compared to our ability to express our thoughts and emotions in words. We all can talk, but interest, application, and experience are necessary to master the art of self-expression. Abraham Lincoln and Adlai Stevenson may have been born orators; Charles Laughton and Audrey Hepburn may have a natural gift for acting. But what stirs us when we read the speeches of Lincoln and Stevenson, or when we see and hear Mr. Laughton or Miss Hepburn, is the experienced artist in expression who has cultivated and developed a natural talent.

Experience of many different savors and flavors, aromas and food feels, will cultivate your natural ability to taste what you eat. Are you ready for some adventures with taste?

One of the great taste thrills is within easy reach. It may be in your refrigerator, or else your grocer has it in stock. The treat is

American Camembert. This is not an exotic cheese. Nor, strictly speaking, is it an imitation of the French Camembert although it is of the same family and probably was intended to provide us with a less expensive version of the imported cheese. If it had been named by its originators Wisconsonia or Albany Cheese, Americans would embrace it as a fellow countryman, as native as Philadelphia Cream Cheese or good golden American. Maxim, the headwaiter of one of the great French restaurants in New York City, with whom I have had long and learned discussions, agreed with me that American Camembert, a standardized product available in every chain store, is superior to the imported French Camembert which anyway does not resemble in the least the Camembert that Frenchmen—and you and I when we travel—enjoy in France.

To use this fine cheese for a taste experiment, buy from your grocer one of those semicircular boxes containing three wedges. Take one of these wedges out of the box, unwrap it, and leave it on a dish under an inverted drinking glass on the kitchen table. Wait for two hours (in the summer, one). Then, without bread and butter, taste one of the refrigerator Camemberts. Clean your taste with a crust of bread. Now taste a morsel from the "liberated" nonrefrigerated wedge.

Do you observe a difference? Of course you do. You may be sure you will never forget it. It is the difference between one of the greatest cheeses ever made in this world—and a cheese too cold to *taste*. They are, remember, the same cheese out of the same box.

If you do not happen to share my fondness for cheese, you can make your first taste experiment with some other food, a favorite of your own such as perhaps grapes or radishes or orange juice. Take one bite or sip of your choice, clean your taste, and eat or drink another bit of the same that has been out of the refrigerator for a while. You cannot help *tasting* the difference—and at the same time enjoying the improvement in the taste of something you like.

You will soon agree with Maxim and me and many others who have made this discovery, that the secret of taste in many foods is *taste liberation*. The refrigerator is one of America's great contributions to the kitchen and the art of eating. It preserves for us the nutritive values and also the authentic natural tastes of foods, by sealing them in with cold. But when we eat the food, we no longer want the taste sealed in; we want it unlocked to the palate. No food but ice cream is at its best eaten right out of the refrigerator, and even ice cream, if frozen hard, is improved with a little rise in temperature.

If you are fond of bananas, taste a banana whose skin is still bright yellow, and another with a brown-flecked or even a totally brown skin. (Remember Chiquita's warning, however, and do not put a banana in the refrigerator even for your taste experiment.) That noble American fruit, the grapefruit, can give your taste buds a whole scale of exercises. Taste half a grapefruit with the sections uncut from their partitions, then cut and taste again. Taste it straight from the refrigerator, and taste it at room temperature; broil it with a little brown sugar and butter on top and have it for dessert, medium hot. Taste the juice of the grapefruit freshly squeezed; in season this may not be too great a luxury. Pour the canned juice straight from the can into your glass and taste; pour it back and forth in two glasses several times to mix it thoroughly with air and taste again. Taste grapefruit juice, fresh, frozen, or canned, thoroughly chilled, and taste it when it has been out of the refrigerator long enough to be cooler than room temperature but not so cold that the palate is shocked by its temperature rather than pleased by its taste.

Foods can be too hot to taste as well as too cold. Many have learned to let their soup or coffee cool a little, so that they can enjoy it. Hot foods should of course be hot when they come to the table, but not so hot as to shock the palate out of its proper function of *tasting*. If you are one of those who boast of having a "cast-iron throat" and habitually take your coffee scalding hot, just once try a good, freshly brewed cup of it a little cooler. The difference between too hot and exactly hot enough is probably not more than a few degrees, but it makes all the difference in the taste.

Some tastes, good in themselves, kill other tastes. We can enjoy both the powerful and the delicate, but not together, unless we remember to "clean the palate" as the professional wine and tea tasters do, with a morsel of bread crust. People who like wine with dinner discover that wine loses its character if sipped with or after salad. Peppery or tangy or fruity sauces like cranberry sauce overshadow the taste of the following dish.

Whisky is a taste-killer when taken with food; this is why most of us take our drink before dinner. Eating the one and enjoying the other are more to the Slim Gourmet's liking than a whisky taboo. If you are one of the few who take your highball to the dinner table, no matter. Simply remember to "clean the palate" before you take up fork or spoon, so that you can eat with the full pleasure of tasting what you eat.

The best taste cleaners in my experience are bread and green olives. They neutralize and prepare the appetite for the next taste pleasure. A crust of bread well chewed does wonders, so does an olive, and a hostess does well to provide both if she wishes her guests to enjoy thoroughly the meal she has so carefully planned and prepared.

A few years ago in a Midwestern city I enjoyed a memorable lesson in taste education. I was the guest of a lady who collects French impressionist paintings. Her second enthusiasm is fine hams. She grieved over the many Americans who eat ham several times a week, usually smothered between two slices of bread, and never really taste the fruit of all the care and inventiveness that go into curing and smoking and aging this venerable friend of gourmets the world over.

She told us everything worth knowing about old English gammon hocks and Wiltshire sides and how vinegar and cloves, pineapple and brown sugar and molasses, help to transform a mere ham into a mouth-watering culinary poem.

Then we were treated to a ham-sampling. We were served tiny slices of Kentucky ham, sweet pickled cured country ham, Tennessee Mountain ham and manly Westphalian *prosciutto di Parma*, and juicy ham from Prague. We tasted ham from the Ardennes, from York in England, and from Toulouse, butts from Boston, and a four-year-old masterpiece of a ham from Smithfield, Virginia. Some of us liked one ham better than another, but all were different, all interesting. Between tastes we ate little pieces of Westphalian pumpernickel to "clean the palate" and sipped on American vodka that was in our hostess's opinion the ideal drink to enhance the taste of any ham.

Neatly trimming the fat from my portions, I did not spend more than 400 calories on this ham-tasting experience, and rarely have I invested my calories so well.

Nobody had to eat much that afternoon. To ask for a second helping never occurred to us. We were enjoying *taste* and did not need quantity to feel satisfied.

Behind our hostess's chair hung a most delicate water color by Cézanne. Nobody would think of saying, "I only like a Cézanne twice that size." Neither would any of the guests have thought of asking for twice as much ham. The educated taste never needs to be a slave to gluttony. Eating for taste, we no longer depend like animals on the mechanical satisfaction of stuffing ourselves full. (But even an animal does not overeat; he merely eats all he can at the time food is there, since unlike human beings he cannot be sure when he will have his next meal.) The more you succeed in refining your taste, the more you enjoy your meals and the less dangerous they become to your weight.

My Midwestern ham lesson I shall never forget. Nor shall I forget a lesson in mushrooms I learned from Eidy, the gay head waitress at the Chesa Veglia Restaurant in St. Moritz.

Serving us a tasty dish of broiled chanterelles which had been freshly plucked, she entertained a whole company of Americans for an hour with her account of the many kinds of edible mushrooms that the Swiss find in their woods and fields during September and October.

Some of us heard for the first time of the morel, the beefsteak fungus which looks like a steak growing out of a tree and tastes like old wine. She brought us pictures of the giant puffball, of the edible parasol, of dozens of other strange-looking but delectable mushrooms which are the delight of Swiss gourmets. During our stay in St. Moritz we were served a number of them. This unexpected new vista in eating experience did not end in Switzerland. On returning home we found we could buy many of these exotic, uniquely flavored mushrooms from Switzerland, France, and Italy, in dried form, in some supermarkets right in the United States. So our lesson in mushrooms has brought continued new tastes to our dinner table at home.

Curiosity, the motor of progress, set the sails of Leif Ericson and Columbus and Magellan, led Socrates to ask the first philosophical questions, and Pythagoras to look for the laws of geometry. Curiosity also brought the fishes, animals, and birds, the vegetables, fruits, and grains to our tables. That unique woman whose inquisitiveness added apples to our diet is the only one of these innovators still known to us by name. Apart from Mother Eve, no record remains of the countless benefactors of humanity who out of curiosity—with perhaps a smattering of hunger—first ate oysters and artichokes, turkeys and kumquats, strawberries, walnuts, and trout, who baked the first bread, made the first cheese, and pressed the first wine.

We take for granted the wide wonderful choice of food and drink their curiosity discovered for us, so much that we forget to be curious ourselves and are content to eat the same well-known staple foods day after day. We carry the same shopping list to the supermarket and give the same order in a restaurant.

We read a menu card as if eating were a painful duty which we can get through only if we are lucky enough to find a tried and familiar dish.

It is a pity. The first sip of tangerine juice, the new taste of turkey stuffed with Steinpilze (a kind of mushroom), can be as wonderful as the first time you wear a new hat or drive a new car.

We are all, without exception, brought up within limited food boundaries and have large blank areas of unexplored food territories on our individual eating maps. I was amazed to learn from my many correspondents how few American families eat fruits in variety, and to discover that out of some thirty housewives none had more than one variety of tea in her kitchen. Few of them even knew that tea can have many tastes. They were astonished at the difference between a smoky Lapsang Souchong and an Earl Grey, a Young Hysong and an English Breakfast tea. The next time you buy tea, instead of getting one pound of one kind, I suggest that you buy four different varieties or blends (not brands) and enjoy a tea-tasting excursion in your own home.

(Note to tea-tasters: Tea yields its flavor fully only when brewed, the boiling water poured directly over the tea leaves and covered to steep for a few minutes. The tea you can buy in tea bags is limited to a few routine blends, and tea bags do not do justice even to these. The pale pigment dripping from a tired tea bag into a cup of hot water has no resemblance to tea except in color, and then only a faint one. The tea bag is an offense against a noble, heartening, and time-honored beverage. Those who like to drink slightly colored hot water, with or without sugar and lemon or cream, may keep their tea bags, but those who would discover the joy of drinking real tea will buy a little teapot when they next go shopping.)

Meats offer taste experiences undiscovered by most Americans. Almost any butcher shop has on its wall a map that can guide the taste explorer. How many cuts of beef, pork, calf, and lamb on that map are unfamiliar to you?

Sweetbreads, one of the great delicacies of French tables, are unknown in vast areas of this country. Calves' liver appeared on many of my correspondents' lists of food dislikes; can it be they do not know how to prepare it? Oxtail, beef kidney, mutton chops, beef tongue, lamb shanks, veal shoulder roasts, pork spareribs, corned beef are omitted from many shopping lists for no good reason. After a while the family comes to believe that beef is the only edible meat, and hamburger, pot roast, and steak are its only edible parts. They lose the taste and eat only the quantity.

There is scarcely a household in America that does not sacrifice taste through routine buying and habitual eating. Like any other human faculty, taste withers if it is not encouraged, exercised, and offered new experiences and enjoyments from time to time.

To develop taste to the fullest is an aim never to be completely achieved. That, too, is good and natural. As your ear is never satisfied and will never signal, "I have heard enough enjoyable music," so your taste will never declare to you, "I have sampled enough delicious food."

4   FOOD CHARACTER

AND EATING PERSONALITY

Can you imagine Falstaff on a diet of carrot sticks and cottage cheese? Cleopatra a vegetarian? G. B. Shaw on a steak and beer diet?

The food ways and eating habits of people go together with their personalities. It has been said that we are what we eat. One can also say that we eat as we are.

Our ways of eating, like all our ways, are handed down to us, parents to children. They are influenced by history, tradition, economics; by family customs and professions; by where we live and how we work; by how we are educated not only in school but also by the advertising pages of our newspapers and magazines, and the commercials we think we do not listen to on radio and television.

From all this we have fairly good indications of the sources of our habits, but there remains in everyone something more that cannot be explained. The something more is the very personal and not so logical behavior that singles each of us out from the crowd and makes what is good for others not so good for ourselves.

Not long ago, in response to a series of newspaper articles, I received some fifteen thousand letters from people in all parts of this country and from Americans overseas, describing to me their individual habits, their likes and dislikes in food, their menus and their diet history, their open and their hidden food wishes. When I tried to classify them, I was often at a loss to place their letters in any kind of category.

Here were fifteen thousand men and women, young and old, tall and small, from New England and from Texas, from California and the Middle West, from the South and from the Mountain States; people of different descents, of a great variety of occupations—and of fifteen thousand food characters.

All these people wrote me because each had the earnest desire to develop a new food personality, one which would help him to escape from his plight. Each of them was struggling with overweight.

I was fully aware that there was no single prescription to give them. There had to be fifteen thousand prescriptions, because there were fifteen thousand personal reasons why these people had gained their weight and there were fifteen thousand individual ways to lose it.

All I could do in my answers was to make them think of themselves as individuals. I could show each one how to work out his own salvation by understanding his own food personality and learning to develop it in more satisfactory directions.

Observations of thousands of people, investigations by psychologists and psychiatrists, psychoanalysts and anthropologists, give me no reason to doubt that every human being is born with a clear, determined, and unchangeable food character. Every one of us has likes and hates of his own; each knows foods and dishes which are agreeable to him and others which he abhors and which do not agree with him.

In the little book, *After Strange Gods*, the American-British poet T. S. Eliot makes a similar observation. "I suppose," he writes, "that everything we eat has some other effect upon us than merely the taste and mastication; it affects us during the process of assimilation and digestion."

This question still is a riddle to medical science. Medicine has not yet fully explained the strange behavior of many human beings in the case of the so-called allergies. The word *allergy* is taken from the Greek and means "strange disease." Strange it is that hives, headaches, swellings, nausea, and asthma can be produced by the eating of such innocuous foods as milk, cabbage, wheat, eggs, tomatoes, oranges, or even by the smell of strawberries.

What we can learn from this is that the food character of any particular man, woman, or child cannot be fully explained by the many influences of tradition and environment. It may also vary according to biological conditions, unknown changes in the cells, chemical reactions in the body, minute differences in the functioning of glands and inner organs. In the light of today's psychosomatic findings we must also include individual differences in emotional makeup, in temperament.

Look around among your friends and you will find many

evidences of this irrational and permanent food character in every person. It can be seen even in the reaction of babies and small children to certain foods. John likes chocolate and Jerry doesn't touch it. Why? They have the same parents. They live in the same house. They are both less than four years old and were brought up in identically the same way.

The young child begins early to show his food character. As he grows older he is subjected to the influences of environment, of habits and customs in the family and later outside of the home. On the foundation of his own separate and original food character there is thus slowly built up the food personality which each of us discovers in himself when he begins to observe his own habits and ways of eating.

This food personality is no longer irrational. We can discover *why* we like spaghetti and *why* we eat turkey on Thanksgiving and *why* we like the traditional Christmas foods at Christmas time.

We can change many of our eating patterns without much difficulty. But we cannot change—and should not ignore—our basic food character.

On the contrary, we have to take our food character very much into account when we decide how we are going to develop our food personality. Any attempt to force ourselves into some eating behavior that is contrary to our food character has the seed of failure in it. I think there is more wisdom in the saying, "One man's meat is another man's poison," than in many scientific dissertations.

Many people believe that one has only to follow one's instincts, to "eat what the body needs," in order to achieve a wholesome and balanced diet. This may be so, but we of the twentieth century are a long way from Mother Nature and the sound of her voice is drowned out by many man-made sounds. I doubt that I could recognize any appetite of mine as instinctive.

Even laboratory rats, as in the experiments of Paul Thomas

Young, have been observed to eat what they like instead of what would cure their man-induced vitamin deficiency. Perhaps we could automatically achieve healthy and pleasant eating by following our instincts—if we could only find them!

And so, reluctant as we may be to recognize it, there seems to be only one solution: we really must apply our minds and our thinking to our eating. That is the only way which leads to health and comfort and the loss of extra pounds.

We may not be able to change our food character. But we can analyze and recognize it and use that knowledge for the development of a pleasure-giving, health-giving food personality.

Not everyone is comfortable in the skin of his own food personality. I have discovered this by observing people's behavior with a restaurant menu card.

One person in a hundred studies the menu card conscientiously, thinks a little, and gives the waiter a firm order for a well-composed meal in tune with his habits, his desires, and his needs. Many of us, however, read the menu card like a book on advanced physics. To choose what we will eat seems a disagreeable task foisted on us by life. Hesitation, insecurity, and fear of the waiter eventually result in a hasty order that makes little sense and does not satisfy even the diner who gave the order.

These are the people with weak food personalities, who are not masters of their eating but slaves of the need to eat. They choose and eat mechanically, fulfilling a duty instead of giving thought to and enjoying one of the most important and most generally available (at least in the United States) pleasures of living. They are trying to follow some diet, perhaps, or to imitate some eating pattern which is not theirs. They have not learned the language of the appetite and are not aware of having a food character. They do not follow the guidance of their own tastes and their own wishes.

Let us see from an example what a food personality can be, and also how it can be changed. Mrs. L., the wife of a New

York advertising man, brought from her native New Orleans all the knowledge of good eating that is the pride of Louisiana. Her food character is rather special. She loves to sit long at the dinner table, whether she is alone with her husband or in company. She looks upon food as the accompanying music to conversation and companionship. She is not rich but she likes rare and exotic foods.

During the day she eats little: coffee and buttered toast for breakfast, the same plus a slice of apple pie for lunch. Her eating life centers around the evening meal; she spends hours in the cooking, preparing four or five courses for a dinner that is rich, surprising, and delightful. She uses many cookbooks and has a collection of books on nutrition and food.

One cannot say that this young woman does not have a food personality. On the contrary, it is a strong and well-formed one. But during four years she gained twelve pounds, and she continued to gain. Out of her numerous books she tried to plan a system that would allow her to live as she likes and at the same time lose her excess weight—without success.

What would you advise in such a case?

Would you abolish the wonderful evening meal, the glory of Mrs. L.'s home life and the source of so much satisfaction to her in the preparation and in the eating? Would you tell this young woman, who knew very well what she wanted in food and who has enjoyed eating all her life, that she should redistribute her allotted eighteen hundred calories over three meals a day, six hundred to a meal? That would certainly be sensible advice from a nutritionist's point of view. But it would change a rich food personality into an unhappy woman.

The Slim Gourmet's solution was simple and rather surprising. We discovered that her food knowledge had one flaw. She knew too little about sauces! While she knew hundreds of recipes and cooked according to many good cookbooks, she always came back to the same three sauces: Sauce Béarnaise, Sauce Hollandaise, and Sauce Robert. These appeared whenever a recipe allowed. And when one of these was on the table, she ate what was in the sauce dish *down to the last drop.*

Obviously these three sauces had a meaning for her beyond their taste. She discovered, as she looked for the reason, that these three sauces had been served regularly at the house of an aunt whom she had visited frequently in her childhood, and whose cooking she had considered the acme of culinary culture. Her aunt's favorite sauces had become a symbol to her. Eating them meant eating good food. It may also have meant—as a psychiatrist might point out—a moment's nostalgic return to the happiness of visiting her aunt in childhood. With such associations she could hardly resist emptying the sauce dish!

Our aim, then, was not to destroy her fine pleasure in food, but to make her emotional sprees with her three sauces infrequent enough so that they would not have so distressing an effect on her weight. Together we made a study of sauces. There is no question in the whole realm of gastronomy so much disputed and discussed as: "What's in a sauce?" For hundreds of years the pride of every chef has been his inventiveness and technique with sauces.

Mrs. L. found the study of sauces fascinating. I gave her the remarkable book by André Simon, *Sauces,* containing the recipes of nearly two hundred of them. Incredible as it may sound to novices in the art of the Slim Gourmet, with the enlargement of her sauce vocabulary Mrs. L. not only stopped gaining weight but slowly lost what she had gained over the years.

She may have learned from our conversations a few more of the ways of the Slim Gourmet. Other little changes may have helped her to turn from gaining weight to losing. In Mrs. L.'s opinion, however, the change is "all in the sauces."

Even so original a food personality could be cultivated for slimness, not by depriving her of the fine foods she loved, but by increasing her enjoyment: in her case, by enlarging her vocabulary of sauces. It is not a device to be recommended to many, for the Slim Gourmet is dedicated to the cultivation of natural taste. But need we say it again? Eating is a personal matter, and if Mrs. L. enjoys her sauces, sauces she shall have.

5 "I KNOW WHAT I LIKE"

"I may not know much about it but I know what I like," we say. We say it about art, music, about the furniture or the color scheme the interior decorator presses upon us. But when it comes to food, we think we know all we need to know about it, and we are quite positive that we know what we like.

Do we, really? Do you? Of the foods you have eaten in your lifetime, I don't doubt that you know which you like and which you dislike—but how many have you tried? How many dishes from your own cookbooks have you eaten or at least tasted? How many new dishes have you ordered from a restaurant menu card in the past year? How many of the thousands of items on your chain store's or your grocer's shelves have you once taken home to try out?

If you are like most shoppers, you have bought the same twenty or twenty-five items, year in and year out, with some slight changes for the seasonal foods, and there are fewer seasonal changes each year. Grandmother's grocer may have had only a few hundred items in his store, of which she also bought only twenty, but they were likely to be a different twenty every few weeks. Fresh fruits and vegetables, some fishes and even some meats were available only at certain times of the year. She was obliged to vary her family's diet. Today, with modern storage and distribution, you and I can eat the identical menu every day of the year if we like. Alas, many of us come close to doing it.

Most of us eat not what we like but what we are used to, what we are limited to by our environment, our experience, and some strange quirks of human nature besides. The limitations of environment we must all accept to some degree. If Hawaiian poi is not to be had in Cincinnati, a Cincinnatian cannot be expected to know the taste of it unless he is lucky enough to take a trip to Honolulu. Human nature enters when he is in Honolulu and declines to try the strange new dish even then. We need to liberate the eating *I* from the chains of food prejudice, food timidity, and simple food ignorance, that keep us from eating with joy and remaining slim.

For years, of all the fruit juices I drank only orange juice. I had learned somewhere that it would help my slimming. Then I discovered that my twelve-ounce glass of orange juice contained 150 calories, and that on most days I was drinking down 300 to 450 calories. Shocked, I began to explore other juices. I discovered quite a vocabulary of them.

When I began to drink juices for taste my glasses became smaller. I chose wine glasses for my juice drinking and of most of the juices I liked—of the many I tried, at least ten became permanent friends—this portion meant only 50 calories. From being an orange juice addict I became a many-juice Slim Gourmet. I drank tangerine and apricot juice, prune juice and grape juice, tomato juice and vegetable juice, at breakfast as well as other times of day. I even became an expert in the various brands of frozen and canned juices. The enlargement of my juice vocabulary alone relieved me of pounds and pounds of excess weight.

Probably you know someone like my friend J., whom I call an always-or-never man. He always wears rubbers when it rains, and never wears a hat. He always goes to the same barber and doesn't need to tell the barber what to do because he always has exactly the same service, never varying it with a shampoo, perhaps, or a face massage. He is the same with food. He always has two scrambled eggs for breakfast, never for any other meal, or prepared in any other way. He never eats salad, never touches certain vegetables, and always orders the same dish when eating out.

Some people who are thus hedged about with habit announce their self-imposed limitation as though it were a point of pride. "No broccoli, thanks—never use it—" "I always take rye—never bothered to try any other drink—I know what I like." To be able to say, "I always—" or "I never—" seems to indicate a strength of character or a uniqueness of personality which perhaps they are fearful they might not have otherwise. But surely it is not a sign of weakness to vary and experiment, to change and to seek out new experience. On the contrary, perhaps it is a sign of strength when one can afford to try out new ways.

Sometimes the fixed personality is not sought but forced upon one. Our nearest and dearest may unintentionally do this to us. A man to whom fish is never served in his own home ("My husband can't endure fish!") ate pompano at our house one evening. His wife was certain he did so only to be polite, until he innocently suggested that she ask for the recipe.

We complain of monotony in our lives and go to some trouble and expense to seek a change—a trip, a new program on television, a new game to take the place of canasta, a new leisure-time hobby, a new hat for Easter or just because we would like a new hat. Meanwhile, right at the table, three times a day and seven days a week, we have a chance for change and newness.

Spring eating can be different from fall eating, Wednesday different from Monday, and next Wednesday different again. Americans have discovered the adventure of eating a barbecue in the back yard, a picnic in the country, a buffet supper in the living room, and for these excursions out of the traditional dining room they have had the reward of fresh pleasures in eating. They have many adventures in eating yet to discover.

Our experiences with food in childhood leave strong marks. A whole generation of Americans grew up with a loathing for spinach, which was "good for you" (it has since been labeled "bad for you" by a new school of nutrition experts as arbitrary as the first). The spinach antipathy was so infectious that it spread to include other greens like beet tops and kale, even the innocent broccoli. In letters I have received, when strong food dislikes were mentioned, broccoli was usually one of them.

I myself do not enjoy goose because my uncle who raised geese kept us too liberally supplied. I do not even care for goose liver pâté, or the red cabbage that is traditional with goose. A friend of mine cannot endure lamb stew, a favorite of his father's which appeared often on the family table. Another friend eats, not one or two frankfurters at a time, but five or six, because his mother never would allow her children frankfurters or indeed any delicatessen fare at all. Sometimes it requires a real effort to free ourselves from what our parents fed us—or, contrarily, what they did not feed us—and become independent adults in our eating.

Foods also have social status. Many of us unconsciously avoid one or another food because it has associations of low social or economic standing. Turnips are considered by many a poor man's food, but they are excellent with roast mutton (excellent, too, for their low calories). The Italians brought with them to this country many of the eating ways of Lucullus and the Roman master cook Apicius, but for a long time Italian foods were scorned by other Americans. The salami and bread that the Italian workman ate for lunch beside the road he was digging was associated with his immigrant status. Today Italian salami is a delicacy on the hors d'oeuvres tray, Italian bread is a treat, and Italian restaurants flourish everywhere.

In the United States food no longer recognizes geography.

Turnip greens and black-eye peas are traditionally Southern foods, but Southerners have moved to Northern cities following the call of industry. Now frozen turnip greens and dried black-eye peas appear in Northern chain stores. You who were born in Cleveland or Detroit, and I who live in New York, can enjoy them even though our mothers never had them in their kitchens.

What makes a rich or a poor food personality? I have known men who love to fish for sport. They know their rainbow trout and their salmon trout, their brook trout and lake trout. They know their black bass and striped bass and calico bass and small-mouthed and large-mouthed bass and also their sea bass. But when it comes to eating they know no fish at all, or perhaps only swordfish. They are rich fishing personalities but poor food personalities.

We had guests to dinner one night, for whom we made rather special preparations. Among them was a lady who is the richest food personality I know. Dining out with friends, she is disappointed when her dinner companions duplicate each other's orders because her great pleasure is to taste from each one's platter. Even at the same meal she likes to savor many dishes. For her special enjoyment, this was our menu for four:

first course: jellied Madrilène for everyone
second course: pâté for one diner
                   poached eggs with ham for the second
                   asparagus with truffles for the third
                   cold jellied carp for the fourth
third course: roast chicken with two vegetables for everyone
fourth course: ice cream with strawberries for one diner
                   fruit cup with kirsch for the second
                   peach in red wine for the third
                   wine custard for the fourth

Not only our lady gourmet but every diner at the table sampled all these dishes, and we all enjoyed four dinners in one. It was, of course, a special treat, which the cook and the kitchen would not be able to produce every night. I offer it only as an example of the pleasures a rich eating personality can enjoy.

And, further proof of my argument, the lady who samples the most and takes the most pleasure in taste is one of the Slimmest Gourmets of my acquaintance. The rich eating personality enjoys eating to the utmost, but he or she is rarely overweight.

6   SCIENTIFIC NUTRITION—

OR GOOD EATING?

Why do menu cards read: "Charcoal-broiled sizzling sirloin steak" instead of "niacin-rich high-protein phosphorus-quantity steak?"

Why does your grocer recommend "the first oranges of the new Florida crop" instead of "Vitamin-C-supplying oranges"? And why do I spend a full hundred calories for that little piece of chocolate-coated candy when for the same number of calories I could eat thirty-three spears of asparagus or ten cucumbers?

Is it because I am not a calculating machine but a human being? Is it because my life is not motivated by science but by desire and appetite? Is it because I eat not only for my health and nourishment but also for other more obscure but equally important satisfactions?

If that is so, is it good? Or is it bad? Do I have to change and how shall I change?

The scientists have done a wonderful job in the past fifty

years or so, discovering what is essential for good nutrition. But some impassioned propagandists for science apparently want us to eat with scale, yardstick, and calorie meter, forgetting about our appetites and obeying only charts and statistics. Reducers especially are warned that they must have their 1.2 mg. of thiamine and 5,000 units of Vitamin C this very day. Against the protest of palate and appetite they must eat a quantity of raw carrots daily because carrots have 3,000 units of Vitamin A to the ounce.

Thus pleasure gives way to anxiety at the table. Have I had enough calcium? Too much? What did I do today about niacin? Will a day without enough iron harm my health? Did I drink enough milk, other fluids, fruit juice?

Much of our so-called "scientific" eating is really based on very little exact knowledge, and the advice that science gives us is often contradictory. Lack of calcium in our diet is regretted by the dentist but the doctor warns of over-calcification. For years certain Danish scientists preached that we would be healthier on a very low-protein diet; now the fashion is to recommend a high-protein diet. The scientists have taught us how important protein is to the body, which uses it to create adrenalin, thyroxin, and other indispensable substances as well as new body tissue. But how much protein does the body need each day? A minimum of seventy grams, or three ounces, we are told by some. And, "The question . . . cannot be answered by a definite figure," says a dean of the science of nutrition, Professor Emil Aberhalden of Zurich University.

Vitamins, minerals—our scientists have lifted the curtain on our complicated body chemistry. With every year our knowledge advances. The scientific papers on nutrition make fascinating reading. But at any given moment do we know enough to change the joy of eating to a scientific treatment administered three times daily?

As nutrition advances, psychology advances, and so does the study of people's habits and customs. We have gained new insight, not only into the body's needs, but also into why we eat and how we eat and what emotions are behind our eating. The nutritionist alone is no more capable of telling us how to eat than the biologist alone or the psychologist alone. Each is in possession of only part of the truth.

Suppose we were talking about science and painting. We know a great deal about the chemistry of paints today; we can measure the tonality of color; we can study the psychology of the artist and explore his conscious and subconscious mind. But would we expect a professor of optics or a psychiatrist to teach us how to paint, or teach us the appreciation of painting?

Of course not, you say. But painting is an art, while eating —yes, what is eating?

Is it an occupation, a duty, a diversion, a chemical process?

Is it just possible that eating is an art? And that we can solve our eating problems by recognizing it as an art?

The Slim Gourmet believes that eating *is* an art, one of the most enjoyable, one of the most gratifying and life-embellishing, and surely the most popular and widely practiced of all the arts. It may be in some cases a forgotten art or a neglected one, an art that has to be revived, restudied, and retaught after years of being ignored and also maligned from time to time as a sin, an indulgence, and nowadays as a science.

If eating can be considered an art, then more artistic eating, more cultivated eating, more personal eating may be the way out of bad eating, unhealthy and joyless eating, and eating that adds excess weight.

The reducer on a 1,000-calorie diet has good reason to be anxious about whether he is getting all the nutrients his body needs. He would do well to worry even more about the nutrients his emotions and his personality might need on such a diet. But those who reduce the Slim Gourmet's way, by regarding eating as an art, need have no such worry.

Artists do not paint in a single color. Artistic eaters combine the fruits and the meats, the vegetables and the fishes, the green and the yellow into a well-proportioned harmony. They respond to the guidance of science, but they eat venturesomely and imaginatively; their motive is not fear but the search for enjoyment and the interest in taste, which keeps them slim.

The reducer who follows the Slim Gourmet's way needs no pills for vitamins, calcium, or iron. Nature provides him with all he needs in the variety of foods he eats even while he reduces. He would rather have his calcium in a cube of good cheddar cheese than in a pill.

The nutritionist's lists of high-value foods are often misleading in their emphasis on one or another source of an essential nutrient. Memory becomes confused, and we come to believe that only carrots can give us Vitamin A, only oranges and grapefruit Vitamin C. Nature offers us what we need in a great variety of foods.

For those of us who are accustomed to reading the ordinary list of basic foods, there may be some surprises in this list, which also gives the most generous sources of essential nutrients. Here are Nature's champion foods, in this order:

The most *calcium* comes in cheese, turnip greens, almonds, kale, water cress, dried figs, egg yolk, broccoli, olives.

The most *phosphorus* comes in cheese, egg yolk, oatmeal, lean beef, chocolate, almonds, whole wheat, peanuts, lentils, liver.

The most *iron* comes in lentils, egg yolk, liver, dried beans, oysters, oatmeal, whole wheat, lean beef.

The most *Vitamin A* comes in calf's liver, beef liver, spinach, turnip greens, cream cheese, mangoes, parsley, beef kidney, mint, butter, papaya.

The most *Vitamin B*^{1} comes in yeast, rice bran, buckwheat, peanuts, bacon, lean pork, brown rice, wheat.

The most *Vitamin C* comes in parsley, black currants, fresh green peppers, Brussels sprouts, horseradish, turnip greens, spinach, broccoli, lemon juice, strawberries, mint, orange juice, water cress, cauliflower.

The most *Vitamin D* comes in herring, sardines, salmon, eel, turbot, butter, fresh cream.

7 THE PHILOSOPHY OF NATURAL TASTE

A Roman cookbook of the third century, one of the oldest cookbooks we know, is the *Kitchen Manual* of Apicius. It describes few simple dishes but many pâtés, preserves, confitures, spiced sauces, combination soups, hash, and salmis—those highly seasoned stews of game in wine.

A roast suckling pig was never merely roast pork. It had to be filled with capers and snipes, goose livers and quails, thrushes and kidneys, truffles and oysters, cherries and grapes, and eaten with a sauce containing so much cinnamon, pepper, honey, garlic, and rare Oriental spices that it would please only people with palates of leather.

I once counted the calories in Petronius's "Meal of Trimalchio"—it came to 11,000. A normal feast-day dinner as described by Pliny would be between 6,000 and 8,000 calories. How the old Romans managed all these calories, even with their baths and massages, we don't know, but we know that we can't manage them. A 6,000-calorie dinner would be a disaster to most of us in the twentieth century.

Why did Lucullus eat this way? Why did Augustus and Pliny, Ovid and Tacitus and Marcus Aurelius, who in every other respect were examples of sanity, good citizenship, and common sense?

The answer is not difficult to find. Caesar's oysters came from

Brittany, Caligula's hams from Westphalia. Nero's goose livers, for which there were not even, in those days, airtight pottery containers, were probably Alsatian.

Imagine if you can the taste of Colchester oysters after a journey of twenty days, even in winter, or the color of a ham that has traveled across half of Europe between January and March by cart or pack animal. What alternative was left to Master Apicius except to make a powerful sauce for the ham and mix the bitter, strong-smelling oyster with neutralizing chestnuts?

Mme. de Sévigné, the great seventeenth-century gossip who poured her confidences into letters and her venom into parentheses, reports that Vatel, Prince Condé's cook, killed himself because a turbot ordered for the King did not arrive in time.

I don't know whether this Vatel ever existed. The legend of his suicide survives, and with it the evidence that even a king could not have his turbot because the Palace of Chantilly had no storage facilities for fresh food. In those days only the king and his nobles could enjoy the privilege of fresh fish, and then only when it was brought by special couriers from the sea to Paris. Royalty ate their food in perhaps a slightly less decomposed state than ordinary city-dwellers. The legendary Vatel and his famous successors had to invent the two hundred sauces, five hundred pâtés, and countless other concoctions to dress up the imperfect taste of the raw materials and hide a decomposition that had begun even before the food reached the kitchen.

Yet we today take these desperate devices as immutable law. Our cookbooks bow down before the sauces we no longer need, which smother the fine natural tastes of our fresh foods and add unwanted and uncounted calories to our eating.

The gourmets of the seventeenth and eighteenth centuries, who created many of the food traditions we still follow, never savored the delight of a sirloin steak as we can eat it, barbecued on charcoal with the tang of hickory smoke. They never could regale their guests with fresh strawberries in January, mushrooms in July, oranges the year round. Their cooks, whether named Vatel or Carême or even the great Escoffier, did not have United States inspected prime quality porterhouse, cut from steers especially bred and fed, hung for the right length of time, and transported from Omaha, Kansas City, or Chicago, to New York, where Toots Shor can select the finest cut for the boxing champion or the television star who on his social register has the same status as Louis XIV had on Vatel's.

We live in a world of deep freezing and sterilized canning, of pasteurization and scientific breeding, of controlled planting and upgrading of quality. The American woman in her kitchen today has something to teach even the most celebrated French chef. Escoffier in his heyday at the Savoy in London did not have an infrared broiler, a refrigerator to chill a melon or freeze a sherbet, or even an automatic toaster!

Honor where honor is due: the master cooks of bygone ages mixed and blended whatever foods, spices, and liquors nature and man provided them, and created delicious dishes. But they had to make the best of second-class meats and fishes. We no longer do. We can afford, as they could not, the taste of the fresh and the love of the natural.

There are hundreds of varieties of pears, prunes, shrimps, lobsters, beans, asparagus, available in exquisite freshness in our town markets. Who has made it his task to praise and classify them, and teach us the deliciousness of a Bouquet shrimp as distinct from a Lake Ponchartrain shrimp? Or the difference between the Bartlett pear and the Kieffer, the Winter Nelis and the Poire d'Anjou?

The Slim Gourmet appreciates asparagus with the flavor that nature bestowed upon it, and trout that tastes like trout. He abhors frying and pieing and saucing good foods until we no longer know which is veal and which is lobster.

The natural taste of young cucumbers is one of the great thrills of early summer, but we rarely enjoy it because we rarely taste the cucumber in its pure and natural state. We add salt and pepper, oil and vinegar, onions and garlic, Russian or Thousand Island dressing, until it might as well be an aged cucumber left weeks too long on the vine. There are people who have never tasted an apple outside of an apple pie, never been delighted by the natural taste of an egg or of lightly fried calves' liver. Their eggs are always fried or scrambled, their calves' liver breaded; their mushrooms are as firmly wedded to cream sauce as though they grew that way in the woods.

If we eat chicken with mayonnaise, salmon with mayonnaise, asparagus with mayonnaise, and also lobster and tuna and lettuce and tomatoes with mayonnaise, are we eating these good foods or are we eating only mayonnaise with slightly varied trimmings? We are doubly cheated, because we miss the joy of natural tastes and spend unnumbered calories for the deprivation.

Even bread has a natural taste. At dinner at a friend's house one evening, a fresh loaf just delivered from the French bakery around the corner was served with the meal, and there were butter and cottage cheese on the bread-and-butter plates. I asked for a piece of rye bread, and ate both the French and the rye without any adornments, comparing and enjoying the different bread tastes.

"How can you eat bread without butter?" I was asked. In the talk that followed we discovered that of our six table companions, four had never tasted bread as it comes from the bakery. They had been taught that butter belongs to bread as Lucky belongs to Strike. Yet well-baked bread is one of the most delectable tastes and it can be enjoyed by everyone every day. It is true that bread is not strictly a "natural" taste since it is a product of human skill, but I think my bread-tasting experiments belong in this chapter, bread being second nature to all of us when we eat.

Californians have made eating salads a fashion which has conquered the whole country; this is a cultivation of natural taste. The universal vote for steak as America's Taste Treat

Number One is in the same direction. Even the French artists of the kitchen recognize the American talent for discovering and cultivating natural taste. On a French menu, what Americans call "Tartar steak" appears as *biftek à l'Américaine.*

Many Americans are still apologetic about their preference for natural taste. American women, who will give their families the appetizing honesty of boiled beef with boiled onions and turnips and potatoes, will make a *Boeuf Stroganoff* with sour cream and rich mashed potatoes when guests come to dinner. Unknowingly they sacrifice their superior natural taste on the altar of a food etiquette set up by some long-forgotten cookbook authoress who was genteel but no gourmet.

The bowl of cherries that would be a perfect dessert becomes a cheese and cherry pie. Sauces and pie crusts are considered superior to the fine taste nature and the farmer bred into the food we buy. Not only do we lose the taste of the beef and the apple, but we insult the fine old American cheddar cheese by making it play second fiddle to a hamburger or an apple pie.

Who dares to eat the duck as a duck? It is even hard to get in good restaurants. Duck *Bigarade* (with oranges) or à la mode is good, too, but one does not really know the taste of duck until one has eaten it crisp and young, braised or roasted with only some salt and pepper and at the utmost a few rashers of bacon.

And especially what sins are committed by cooks and diners against fish and shellfish! Shrimps, lobsters, crayfish, scallops, crabs, and prawns—these great friends of the Slim Gourmet reveal their delicacy in full only when eaten as they are. Cooked, steamed, or broiled, and served with a sliced lemon and a little butter—that is the respectful way to treat these choicest of all fruits of the sea.

Of course even the Slim Gourmet may now and then try what a lobster becomes when he is cooked in port wine and served with a creamy sauce, but one would hardly consider that eating lobster. That is eating a dish of which lobster is the base and the foundation. It is part of the Slim Gourmet's pleasure in food to know and enjoy both.

A cream sauce hides the subtle flavor of asparagus, the delicate earthiness of the fine artichoke, and the green individuality of leafy spinach. We should not have to break through a sauce barrier to enjoy a young cauliflower's natural sweetness.

The philosophy of natural taste is one of the Slim Gourmet's first aids to enjoyment while slimming. Once we begin to discover the exquisiteness of natural taste and its infinite variety, it is no sacrifice to decline the sauces and concoctions so over-rich in calories.

You might begin your own adventures in natural taste, perhaps by declaring war on French-fried potatoes and trying a baked potato instead. A little butter melting in the flaky whiteness of the baked Idaho, with the added aroma of chopped parsley, a sprig of thyme, or some finely cut spring onion, makes a dish you will not forget.

Eat your next apple as it grew on the tree, your next dish of roast young lamb in its natural juice with a chopped leaf of rosemary. Discard pies for the sake of fruit and put cutlet unbreaded on your menu.

Beware of the à la's on menu cards.

Order a trout "natural taste" and you will enjoy what also helps you to lose weight.

And if you cannot immediately divorce the mayonnaise from your cold lobster, use it with respect for the lobster's kingly taste—one-quarter teaspoon of mayonnaise is enough for a whole lobster.

Read your cookbooks with an eye to your new knowledge of twentieth-century eating. Their artificialism was probably helpful to Grandmother, but it is out of tune with our living habits and the quality of our foods, so much better in our markets than in hers.

Buy the better grades and better qualities wherever you can

obtain them. This is not an uneconomical proposition. The natural-taste kitchen saves so much money on sauces and extraneous food additions that we can easily afford to buy the best and enjoy the choicest.

I have discovered that it pays the Slim Gourmet to eat for natural taste even in the most famous eating places. The celebrated duck *à la presse* at the Tour d'Argent in Paris is a great dish, but their filet mignon is an even greater achievement. It is not so easy to make a good filet mignon. In the hands of a French master cook it can become a poem. So can everything that is prepared with only one view, the Slim Gourmet's view: to bring out the natural taste of nature's gift to humanity, to let meat taste like meat, fish like fish, vegetables like vegetables, and fruit like fruit.

Book Two

THE SLIM GOURMET'S

WAY TO REDUCE

8 REDUCING STARTS WITH PLEASURE

Michel Eyquem de Montaigne was one of the former proprietors of the Château D'Yquem, which produces the greatest sweet wine in the world. That vineyard is remarkable not only as the home of the finest sauterne that money can buy (a bottle of 1904 or 1914 Château D'Yquem is worth its weight in gold). Its owners are exceptional people too. The present proprietor, the Marquis de Lur-Saluces, president of France's Wine Propaganda Bureau, is one of the best-known wine-tasters in the world and a frequent visitor to our shores.

Its sixteenth-century owner, Michel Eyquem (de Montaigne) knew much less of America than his successor, but in the course of his rich life he became a great connoisseur of the human soul. His *Essays* are still among the world's richest treasures for wisdom and common sense, and it has been my habit for many years to dig in Montaigne for human knowledge every night.

He wrote on life and death, on love and war, on politics and government. He thought about justice and religion, rulers and philosophers, living and eating. He also wrote on dieting, and I have found that some of his observations published in the year 1580 are so similar to the Slim Gourmet's philosophy that I must call them to the attention of my readers.

He said, "Change of every kind is disturbing and hurtful. . . . They keep ordering us not merely a new diet, but the very opposite to what we are accustomed to; a change that not even a healthy man can suffer. . . . I have no wish to cure one ill with another; and hate the remedies which are more unpleasant than the malady. . . . I have never taken harm from any action in which I found great pleasure."

Thus spoke a philosopher 375 years ago. The advice of the Slim Gourmet is to follow his thinking, and to begin reducing by thinking of the pleasures it will bring.

When I used to set forth on a new diet every once in a while, it always took me some time to fix a starting date for the diet. The old joke, "Tomorrow I am dieting," applied to me. The reason was obvious. Most diets are studded with forbidden foods. The first thing you read in diet books is *Don't eat* bread, butter, milk, breaded cutlets, sweets, desserts, bananas, nuts, avocados, and so on. Just when I had made my decision to start dieting, one of the forbidden foods turned up and looked so delicious and alluring on the table that I could not resist. So the dieter postpones the beginning of the diet from one day to another until the firm resolution is dissipated.

The Slim Gourmet's way of reducing starts in a different mood. The idea of reducing is quite natural because you are not yourself if you are not near your normal weight. You know that reducing cannot be achieved overnight. It took quite some time for you to assemble the overweight, and to make it disappear permanently will take some time.

Whether you are ten pounds or sixty pounds overweight is immaterial. You will take the same reducing way. This means that every day you will eat about 500 calories less than your daily maintenance calorie allowance permits, and automatically you will lose a pound a week. Should you be ten pounds overweight, your reducing will be over after ten weeks. In case your overweight is sixty pounds, it will take you one year and eight weeks. That's all, and it is nothing to be frightened of because a year's reducing, according to the Slim Gourmet's system, contains so many pleasures that you would easily be able to continue for another year if necessary.

There is no sacrifice and there are no forbidden foods. There are no taboos and nothing is "fattening." So there is no need to postpone the beginning of reducing. You can start immediately by planning some joyful eating for your next meal.

I knew a woman who started her reducing program in the middle of June. She was very fond of asparagus. June is the season when asparagus is at its peak in taste, and fresh asparagus, cooked standing in water, can be a succulent dish. It was quite natural that the first diet meal we planned was asparagus with smoked oxtail.

Another of her favorite foods turned out to be lobster. For dinner the following day, we planned a wonderful cold medium-sized lobster, accompanied by asparagus salad with vinaigrette sauce decorated by little cubes of the whites of hard-boiled egg.

Is this a reducing diet? Of course it is. The six ounces of lobster meat represent no more than 130 calories and twenty stalks of wonderful fresh asparagus in themselves are not more than 70 calories.

There are parts of this country and countries in this world where lobster, asparagus, artichokes, steak, turkey, brook trout, turtle, shrimps, ham, strawberries or whatever you like most are very expensive. I do not think that this should prevent you from beginning your reducing with whatever you like most, even if it is expensive. Consider this a festive meal. Compare it with the money you spend on a birthday or anniversary. You are beginning a new life, a period of better eating, a time of more gracious living. Whatever you eat at home or in a restaurant will be cheaper than a bottle of pills of doubtful value. Pills will give you only the illusion of reducing, and less fun.

Buy whatever you choose from the list of your favorite foods. Buy the best available quality and enjoy it in the knowledge that this is only the first of the new pleasures of the table, which will lead you to efficient and permanent weight reduction.

It sounds simple to say that you should eat 500 calories less than your daily maintenance calorie allowance. Do you know what your daily maintenance calorie allowance is? This is the number of calories you need each day to maintain your weight without losing or gaining. It can be as little as 2,000 calories for a woman of average height and sedentary occupation, or as much as 5,000 for a tall man who does heavy work.

To determine your daily calorie maintenance allowance, first you find your ideal weight according to your sex, age, and physique. (There is a reliable height-weight table in Chapter Nineteen.) Next, decide to which of these activity groups you belong:

If you are (1) sedentary, your key number is 16;
            (2) fairly active, 18;
            (3) very active, 20;
            (4) doing heavy work, 24 up to 34.

Now multiply your ideal weight by your key figure, and you have the number of calories you need per day to maintain your ideal weight.

Which activity group you belong to depends, of course, on the work you do. Heavy workers, in group four, include lumberjacks, stevedores, mountaineers. Group three embraces carpenters, waitresses, farm workers, and farmers' wives. In group two are most people who work at machines or with appliances, such as weavers and housewives, and those who walk a great deal or engage regularly in sports. The sedentary people in group one include most of us who are reading this book: the bank president as well as his wife and most other wives, his secretary, his lawyer, the bank teller, the dress designer and the interior decorator, the accountant and the tax specialist and the senator in Washington.

If you are one of these, your key number is 16. Let us assume that you have looked up your ideal weight and discovered that it is 154 pounds. Multiply this by 16 and you have 2,464 calories, your daily calorie maintenance allowance. Once you reach your ideal weight, this is the number of calories you will need each day to maintain it.

But today, perhaps, your scale has shown you that you are ten pounds over your ideal weight. Ten weeks from now, if you follow the Slim Gourmet's way and lose a pound a week, you will have reached your ideal weight. During these ten weeks you will lose that pound a week by eating 500 calories a day less than your daily maintenance allowance.

Depending on your daily calorie maintenance allowance, your reducing budget is approximately one of these:

SMALL WOMEN 5′ 4″ AND UNDER—1,600 calories per day
SMALL MEN　　 5′ 6″ AND UNDER—1,800 calories per day
TALL WOMEN 5′ 5″ AND ABOVE—1,800 calories per day
TALL MEN　　 5′ 7″ AND ABOVE—2,000 calories per day

These are generous eating allowances. If you are in good health the allowance for your size will be absolutely sufficient to supply you with energy to live as you have lived before and to reduce slowly at the pace of one pound per week. Within your eating allowance you can continue your habitual mode of life. You do not have to change into a completely different food personality.

Your calorie allowance will of course lead you to make certain minor adjustments in your present food habits. But if these adjustments are accompanied by new pleasures at the table, you will not feel them as sacrifices, but rather as steps toward increasing your joy of eating.

The next step in planning your reducing will be the division of calories for your various meals.

Probably you have already observed that you are eating not only the three meals which the usual diet provides, but also some meals in between. Don't forget to take these little meals into consideration. It would be wrong to divide an allowance of 1,800 calories, for instance, into three meals of 600 calories each when you have a midnight snack or afternoon tea or cocktails. This allotment of a certain number of calories to each meal is a useful guide. It may help to give here the calorie allotment which I myself made and on which I reduced from 250 pounds to 168 pounds. I allotted my 2,000 calories thus: breakfast, 350 calories; luncheon, 450 calories; dinner, 900 calories. *For the snacks I reserved 300 calories.*

As you will see, breakfast and dinner are my most important meals and I gave them very generous allowances, whereas the particular pattern of my day made it possible to lunch on only 450 calories without feeling hungry at any moment of the day.

You cannot eat calories. What does this allowance mean in real eating? Here is my program for one reducing day:

At breakfast I had:
    4-oz. glass of tomato juice
    1 slice of pumpernickel with a thin pat of butter
    1 soft-boiled egg
    1 wedge of Camembert cheese
    1 cup of black coffee, which had been brewed particularly well
        in a Chemex filter coffee maker
    Total—350 calories

At luncheon I had:
    shrimp cocktail
    plain omelet

1 cup of coffee with
   cream and sugar
Total—420 calories

*Before dinner I took a sip of whisky (½ oz. was sufficient to give me
a taste) and at dinner I had:*
   consommé
   1 roll with a thin pat of butter
   beef tongue with spinach
   1 baked potato seasoned with spring onion
   fruit salad with Cognac
   1 glass of wine
   Total—850 calories

At bedtime I ate a large apple (red Delicious) with a slice of American cheese which accounted for 250 calories.

If I made no mistake in the size of the portions, all of this came to 1,920 calories—still 80 calories under my daily allowance.

This is of course a very personal way to eat, based upon my personal eating habits and food likes. I need a hearty breakfast and quite a substantial dinner. Others will have a breakfast of only 200 calories, a 700-calorie luncheon, a 700-calorie dinner and a 400-calorie snack.

According to reports, M. L. Curnonsky, prince of the French gastronomes, eats only an egg for breakfast and one or two eggs for luncheon, saving all his available calories for his dinner, which is then quite sumptuous. That is his way of life and as he is a late riser and does very little physical work during the day, it must be healthy for him. He has arrived at his present age of eighty-two years on this regime, and enjoys the best of health.

There are many people who combine breakfast and luncheon. On Sundays this has become a custom. Obviously, special days like Sundays and holidays require a completely different allotment of calories for the various meals.

Here is the caloric meal distribution of a New York taxi

driver with whom I had a lengthy talk on the Slim Gourmet's philosophy and ways of reducing.

His reducing allowance is 1,800 calories and he eats: breakfast, 600 calories; luncheon, 300 calories; during the afternoon, 300 calories; during the evening, 400 calories; at night, 200 calories.

He does not call his evening meal dinner and his night meal a snack because he sits down to only one real meal a day and that is his 600-calorie breakfast, which includes such unusual breakfast dishes as hamburgers, fried flounder, kidney stew, and cheesecake.

Our taxi driver's meals have no resemblance to the dieter's three meals a day. But they suit his irregular working hours, and with them he is happy while reducing. If we want to reduce happily we must tailor our calorie allotments according to our meals as we like them, and follow our habits instead of fighting them.

When you have begun your reducing in a joyful way by eating what you like, fixing your reducing calorie allowance, and dividing it among your meals according to your customary way of eating, you may find that after the first week you have lost one pound, after the second week another pound. By a happy chance you have hit upon the right reducing method for you and need look no further. You can continue as you have begun until the last ounce of overweight has vanished.

It may be that during the first week you lose nothing and during the second week you lose more than a pound. This phenomenon is not unusual. The water economy of the body is still one of the mysteries of metabolism. Because of some difference in your salt intake or some other aspect of your body chemistry it may take a little time until your body reacts to the slight change in eating habits that you have just begun.

There is, on the other hand, the possibility that you may lose more than the pound per week which is the Slim Gourmet's measure and the only sensible way to reduce. In that case, either you are overestimating your calories per portion or you have underestimated your maintenance allowance. If you are under the doctor's care while following the Slim Gourmet's method, ask your doctor what causes this excessive weight loss.

The reason for not losing weight is in most cases a beginner's lack of knowledge of foods, portions, and cooking ingredients. Losing too much weight may be caused by the same lack of knowledge. This was why I lost four extra pounds during my first weeks of reducing. But losing too much weight may also have some medical cause. When you continue to lose two or three pounds instead of one pound per week, it is reason not to rejoice but to ask your doctor.

This chapter has dealt mainly with the calories you should take or leave. We have not yet discussed the foods you are going to eat. The problem of a balanced diet looms large when you are following the rigorous reducing regime of 1,000 calories a day, which necessarily neglects one kind of food and leans too heavily on another.

The Slim Gourmet's system, however, maintains balanced nutrition without the need to worry about vitamins and minerals, without making each meal a mathematical puzzle and each mealtime an anxiety. With 1,600, 1,800, 2,000 or even more calories to spend, and the pursuit of happiness in eating, your diet will be varied and its balance will take care of itself without more than normal sensible attention from you.

Eat what you like. You like mostly what you need, if you follow the Slim Gourmet's philosophy and seek variety and change in your enjoyment of tastes.

9   DISCOVERING YOUR

PERSONAL PORTION SIZE

The average bacon-and-eggs order includes two eggs and two pats of butter. That is about 450 calories, and it is one breakfast too many for most of us, either at the drugstore counter or at home.

Dieters, of course, order no bacon and eggs. They must eat hard-boiled eggs, whether or not they like them, because that is what the diet prescribes. But those who reduce the Slim Gourmet's way are not limited to hard-boiled or any other kind of eggs, or any particular breakfast. They eat what they like!

If you like to start the day with the traditional breakfast, why shouldn't you? Your only restriction is your *personal portion size*. You order your breakfast as you would order your shoes or your new suit: to your own measure. If you are less than six feet tall, you order your bacon with *one* egg.

You wouldn't feed an Austin car with Cadillac quantities of gasoline. The Austin goes forty miles on one gallon, the Cadillac on five.

Mrs. A. writes from Indiana: "I don't eat much. To the dot, I eat the same portions as my husband, and he is lean and slim and I become heavier and heavier. . . ."

And when I ask about their height and occupations, Mrs. A. answers that she measures five feet three inches, and works around the house, while her husband is six feet one inch, and a golf *pro!*

She needs 2,300 calories a day and he needs about 3,400. Mrs. A. is not telling the exact truth. If she were really eating the same portions which her tall husband needs merely to maintain his weight and strength, she would be overeating by 1,100 calories a day and would be in much worse plight than she is. Even so, she confesses to thirty-eight pounds of overweight.

Here is the little Austin refueling like a Cadillac. A good wife wants to feed her husband well. How many good wives sacrifice themselves, unknowingly and unnecessarily, by matching the man-sized portions they give their husbands, forgetting that they are of a different size? They wouldn't try to wear the same size hat or gloves!

Mrs. G., the food editor of a leading Midwestern newspaper, takes a maternal pride in the growing appetite of her fourteen-year-old, baseball-playing son. "Quite naturally he eats more and more and I keep him company: the same dishes, the same portions, and the same size of potatoes and steaks, omelets, and apples. Now I understand why I gained."

Mr. R., the sales manager of a wholesale seed firm in the Northwest, discovered that his business luncheons with some of his tall clients were too much for his five feet seven inches. "I feed them on giant steaks and I always thought steaks were reducing. It seems that is wrong: a one and one-half pound steak gives you one thousand calories and the calorie charts count only six-ounce portions. In the future I will pay more attention to the sizes of everything I eat—and drink."

No two people are alike in their calorie needs. It is good not to forget that at the dinner table, and even to remember it in the kitchen.

I know a house where the husband drinks a ten-ounce glass of milk and his wife drinks half a glass. He eats two poached eggs for breakfast and madam only one. When they eat hamburgers the patties are made in two different sizes. Her dinner plate is served with one slice of the roast and one potato, his with two of each. In that house any guest or member of the family is free to choose his or her *personal portion size*.

This family has learned that you don't gain weight if you are portion conscious. Even cheesecake or ice cream is not "fattening" if you know the size of the portion that is right for you.

Followers of the Slim Gourmet's way know their *personal portion size*. Thus they can eat what they like, eat as often as they like—and reduce without advertising the fact even to their table companions.

When I want to eat "fattening" apple pie, I eat it. The eight- or nine-inch pie is usually cut into six pieces; my PPS for pie is half the average slice. My helping counts for 150 calories instead of the usual 300, and I enjoy my apple pie as much as anyone at the table.

I don't like skimmed milk. Why shouldn't I drink delicious rich whole milk when I know that a four-ounce glass is my PPS? I drink it with pleasure and without guilt; I can easily fit its 90 calories into my budget for the day.

Does a woman buy a raincoat instead of the mink she can't afford? She buys the pretty fur or wool coat that fits her budget and her taste. No more should she eat raw carrots when it is chocolate she craves. With the right PPS she can eat candy if she likes and still reduce or keep her normal weight.

How do you determine your PPS? In a general way it corresponds to your size and your physical activity. For example:

The *large* PPS in a helping of meat, about eight ounces, is for men of more than five feet ten inches, or smaller men who do heavy work; these need more than 2,800 calories a day. Only a few women need this many calories.

The *medium* PPS, about six ounces of meat, is for men between five feet four and five feet ten, for women five feet five or taller, and for teen-agers. All these need between 2,400 and 2,800 calories a day.

The *small* PPS is for women less than five feet five, and for men less than five feet three, provided they do no heavy work or regular athletic exercise; this PPS corresponds to about 2,400 calories a day, or less. It is also for all *reducing* Slim Gourmets.

The small PPS, about four ounces of meat, may be all you need to reduce by. Try it as an experiment: for the next four weeks, eat what you like but keep strictly within your small PPS. If you find you are shedding a pound a week you are on the right path and can continue until you have reached your normal weight. If you are not successful on this first try, you can begin working on some of those habits that have made you gain weight, as you will discover from your Food Habit Inventory, in the next chapter, and the Twenty-One Reasons Why (Chapter Eleven). Let the Weekly Habit-Testers (Chapter Twelve) help you deal with the habits that stand between you and your Slim Gourmet goal.

When you have reached your desired weight you can adopt your permanent PPS. If you follow the guidance of your own PPS, you will never again have to reduce.

Nobody—not the waiter in the restaurant nor the cook at home nor the butcher who supplies your meat—can dictate to you your PPS. Once you have worked out your daily calorie budget and the number of calories you have for each meal, you alone can decide how many of your calories you want to spend for each dish. Your PPS is your key to the pleasure of eating the foods you like while you reduce. It is worth fighting for. It is also worth working out with care.

The calorie chart tells you how many calories a portion of a certain size will cost you. How do you judge the size? A 100-calorie slice of turkey should be 4" x 2½" x ¼". That looks clear enough in print but confusing on the dinner plate. Should you take a tape measure to it? Should you carry a postage scale to meals to be sure your slice of salmon loaf weighs four ounces and not six?

Here are some ways I found to guide me to my PPS:

I checked the sizes of the glasses in our kitchen and our bar. Thus I knew whether I was drinking my fruit juice or cocktail from a four-ounce or a six-ounce glass, my milk or beer from a ten- or a twelve-ounce glass. (I soon decided to drink my beer in a four-ounce wineglass.)

I weighed just once the usual portions of meat and fish served in our house. I learned, for example, that while the calorie chart measures steak in three-ounce or four-ounce portions, at our table the serving was usually eight ounces. During the time when my PPS for reducing was four ounces of steak, I had only to ask for half a portion.

On the basis of my PPS at home I was soon able to judge by eye alone the portions I was served outside the home. Also, as the average size and calorie value of each dish became familiar I found that its size to the eye also became familiar. In a little while I could recognize a portion larger than average, and guide my eating accordingly. Once I recognized the size of one portion it became increasingly easy for me to judge the size of others.

I found it useful to know some average portion sizes served in restaurants. For example, the average restaurant hamburger is six ounces. The average minute steak in American restaurants is three and one-half ounces. An individual small sirloin weighs six ounces, but steaks differ extremely from one restaurant to another, the steak houses especially priding themselves on serving large ones. Some Chicago restaurants serve a one and one-half pound steak to each customer.

The average slice of a roast, whether ham, veal, beef, or pork, measures 4" x 4" x ¼", approximately three and a half ounces. The calorie count varies, of course, according to the meat.

The average portion of steak fish such as halibut, salmon, or swordfish is 4" x 3" x ½", about four ounces. The average small fish served whole, such as butterfish or trout, weighs four ounces. Larger fish served whole, especially in fish and seafood restaurants, such as mackerel or bluefish, are generally between six and eight ounces.

Soups, stews, and casserole dishes are generally served in portions of one cup or eight ounces to a customer.

A helping of vegetables averages one-quarter cup or four tablespoons. Most vegetables, as the calorie chart will show you, are so low in calories that an extra tablespoon or two will make little calorie difference. High-calorie vegetables are mainly the dried peas and beans (baked beans) and, somewhat lower in the calorie scale, fresh or canned corn. Potato calories depend upon how the potatoes are served as well as the size of the portion: fried, creamed, or scalloped potatoes cost more calories than baked or boiled.

Cheeses are easy to judge by eye if you use as a measure a wedge of American Camembert or Swiss Gruyère, which are about equal in dimensions and weigh about one ounce each. A number of cheeses are usually served in wedge, cube, or slice weighing one ounce, and fall within nearly the same calorie range: 110 for Swiss; 100 for Camembert, Brie; 125 for cheddar and Swiss Gruyère. Italian Provolone, a nice cheese with a smoky flavor, is, however, only 50 calories for the same size piece.

Most dessert puddings are served in four-ounce portions, the contents of a custard cup. The average wedge of pie is one-sixth of a nine-inch pie.

As you gain skill in following the Slim Gourmet's way you can adjust your PPS to fit the occasion. You can vary it according to what you feel like eating as well as how many calories you can afford to spend for it. When you order a hamburger and baked potato for your lunch, your PPS may be the whole six-ounce hamburger and half the baked potato, or two-thirds of the hamburger (four ounces) and the whole potato (if it is medium-sized; of a giant Idaho you would eat only half for the same calories).

A scoop of ice cream is 300 calories. When I feel like having ice cream my PPS is half a scoop—I enjoy the same refreshing, cool, sweet-tooth satisfaction for half the calories. The same with pie, with cheesecake: all the fun and half the calories. Half an avocado, the normal portion, is 200 calories. I relish all the taste and texture of this superior food in one quarter of an avocado: 100 calories.

At first, when I needed to measure portions and wanted an

unobtrusive way to do so, I made use of various familiar objects on the table: The bowl of an ordinary tablespoon is 3″ long, of a teaspoon 1½″ (but a tablespoon is equal to three teaspoons in contents). The tines of an ordinary dinner fork are 2½″ long. The regular-size package of book matches that I carry in my pocket is 2″ wide, 1½″ long, ¼″ thick at the thick end.

You will not need these measuring aids for long, however. You carry in your head the prices of many items remembered from shopping and advertisements; without effort you remember many telephone numbers and addresses that you use often. In the same way, in a week or two or three, you find yourself remembering that twenty cherries, one medium-sized apple, a dish of fruit Jello, are all 100-calorie desserts for luncheon. (In the Slim Gourmet's Calorie Chart at the end of this book the measurements are given for 100-calorie portions.) The calorie values of your most familiar foods will come to you automatically and the sizes of your personal portions will be as recognizable as the faces of friends.

10 STRICTLY PERSONAL:

THE FOOD HABIT INVENTORY

In a French magazine I read an article which had not one good word to say about the American cuisine. This writer's main complaint was the conformity of our eating habits. Here is his list of all the dishes Americans eat: the hamburger, the hot dog, roast beef, pot roast, ham and eggs, Virginia ham, fried chicken, doughnuts, ice cream, chocolate layer cake, peanuts, popcorn, coffee, Coca-Cola, sweet rolls, and club sandwiches.

I suppose this gentleman stopped only long enough in the

United States to visit the airport terminal in Idlewild between two planes, and copied from its menu card whatever seemed strange to him. (Even so, his listing gives more choice than is available in many European restaurants!) If he had taken the time to walk along even one principal street in one big or medium-sized city he would have seen block after block literally studded with restaurants of the most varied personalities.

There are steak temples and seafood palaces; there are French and Italian, Chinese and South American restaurants; there are restaurants specializing in chicken only. There are thousands of diners and sandwich counters and hamburger heavens and all do a thriving business.

Who does this Frenchman given to hasty judgment think are the guests in these restaurants, if not Americans of all walks of life? Why do our big American restaurants feature on their elaborate menu cards Chinese and Italian, French and Jewish, Mediterranean and Pacific dishes and more kinds of salads than the menu cards of all the rest of the world put together? Only because Americans, despite the many limitations we have observed, are still the world's most individualistic eaters.

Other wiser Frenchmen have come to quite the opposite conclusion from that of their careless compatriot. In *Le Monde à Table* (*The World at Table*), an "International Gastronomic Guide and Dictionary," the chapter on the United States begins:

"For most Europeans, the United States is a country where people live on pickles and ice cream, and where all cooking can be summed up in one single and universal instrument: the can-opener.

"This is an oversimplified view of the reality. On the contrary, there are few countries where people are more interested in the culinary arts. Cookbooks are published by the thousands whose sumptuous illustrations, streaming with colors, are enough to make your mouth water. All the women's magazines compete to give you savory, decorative, original recipes and to present 'something different for dinner.' " And the chapter ends: "If Americans cling to their culinary customs and their specialties, they nevertheless take a sympathetic interest in the gastronomy of the world. Their curiosity and their appetites know no frontiers. Their typical cuisine is the meeting-place of a peaceful and universal League of Nations."

The free choice of what one will eat is a right and a custom in this free country. If I were asked what I consider the typical American breakfast I would be at a loss to say what it is. But it is easy to give a typical French or English or Dutch breakfast, because in those countries anybody who does not follow the national pattern is considered odd.

The great diversity in American eating makes it hard to deal with any food problem in a general way. Overweight, being a food problem, must be attacked personally and individually. We might be able to tell a Swiss or a Dutchman why he is overweight by looking into the cuisine of his country or his province. Not with an American. My food ways may resemble those of my neighbor, my husband or wife, and my children, but they are also strictly my own, and I must therefore have my own reasons for my overweight.

To find reasons I must analyze my food habits. Only when I know my own particular ways of eating will I be able to put my finger exactly on the spot and say, This is why I have gained weight. There may be not one reason but many. Until I know what they are I will not be able to do anything about my extra pounds.

The simple-minded man in one of Molière's comedies discovered with amazement that he had been speaking prose all his life. Most people are equally astonished, once they begin to chart their food habits, to discover what they have been eating for many years.

The analysis of one's own food habits is the basis of any talk or action or even thinking about overweight. It is the foundation stone of the Slim Gourmet's philosophy. Until you realize how you differ in habits from others, you will not discover why you differ in weight from others. Until you single out the causes for your gaining weight you will not find the way to lose weight.

That is simple logic. But to make it work for you you must do a little work yourself. You will find it interesting, however, to draw the portrait of your own food personality: to make an honest investigation into your likes and dislikes, the meanings food has for you, the satisfactions that you expect food to give you, and the limitations in your food experience which you have taken for granted until now.

You will make some surprising discoveries when you review your open and hidden ideas of good and bad food, of meals that are wholesome and those that are harmful for you, and the often irrational and contradictory food prejudices that you, like all of us, have cherished all your life.

In practical results the exploration of your own food ways will be the most rewarding effort you have ever undertaken in the direction of reaching and keeping your normal weight. To help you do this job with exactness, I offer you the Slim Gourmet's Food Habit Inventory, which I developed in my own search for the cause and cure of my overweight.

The Food Habit Inventory asks you many questions. They are questions which you alone can answer about yourself. If you answer them honestly, at the end you will have an exact self-portrait of your eating personality, which can lead you out of your plight of overweight to the promised land of joy and slimness. Superficial answers, however, will not lead to anything. We are all tempted to cheat a little when we answer questions about ourselves. But here we have no reason to cheat, because we don't have to show our Food Habit Inventory with the answers to anybody at all.

The fear of revealing one's real self, of writing one's habits down honestly on paper, lasts only until the last word in the Inventory has been written. When you read your answers you will see that there is no reason to hide anything from anybody. Food habits are no sin!

Perhaps you have been a victim of one of the high priests of some wonder diet who, while praising one food as an infallible remedy for overweight, in the same breath condemns all other customs, meals, and dishes that have been created for our eating enjoyment. Most people hesitate to write down that they like to eat chocolate bars between meals. They have been taught by these wonder-diet Savonarolas that chocolate is fattening and that for the weight-conscious to eat a piece of chocolate is a sinful indulgence. If there are any sinners in this affair, they are the inventors of the wonder diets. The world became a pleasanter place when man learned to make chocolate, still pleasanter when he learned to make good chocolate, and to pack and distribute it so that we can buy for little money a delicious hunger-stopper that gives us immediate satisfaction even if we eat only a small piece.

You need have no shame in writing down that you eat between meals, that you like an ice cream soda, or coffee and cake, or tea and cinnamon toast in the afternoon, that you have a second breakfast at your desk in the middle of the morning, that you hardly ever go to bed without first paying a visit to the refrigerator. Why should you feel like a naughty child, expecting to be punished? These are your food ways. They bring you pleasure, comfort, relaxation that you need. They cannot be abolished without causing you distress in some degree. Some of them, in fact, can never be abolished. Your sturdy, self-assertive food personality would defend them.

Some of them, of course, contribute to the overweight that now troubles you. It is your present purpose to find out what these weight-accumulating food ways of yours really are, and just how much they contribute to your excess pounds. It will be your next purpose to discover how you can *keep* the pleasant food ways that are comfortable for you, and *not keep the weight*.

The only thing you gain by fighting your food habits is the weight you have dieted to lose. But if you know your food habits, make friends with them, understand them and what they mean to you, you will find that they help you to reach and to retain your normal weight.

Now, please, slowly and carefully peruse these

Instructions to Be Read Before Answering the Food Habit Inventory

Please do not begin unless you have at least one quiet and free hour available. That is the time you will need to answer the questions correctly.

Read the Inventory first from beginning to end without answering any questions.

Take time to think and think again about your answers. We are often not aware of our true behavior and have built up legends about ourselves which we believe to be the truth. We actually believe, for instance, that we eat only two or three meals a day when in reality we eat four, five, sometimes six.

After you have answered the entire Inventory, make the lie detector test. Look at yourself as a doctor would who knows that no one answers such questions without involuntarily rose-coloring the facts. Be severe with your patient. Pin him down on over-optimistic estimates, tidbits he forgot, and questions he answered as he wished the answer to be.

When you have finished, down to the last period on the last answer, do not immediately read the chapter that follows, *Twenty-One Reasons Why People Gain Weight*. First try some detective work on your own. See whether you can find one or more *whys* for your present weight. The discoveries that you make yourself are the ones that count most.

There is no reason why you should not be able, after having filled out an honest Food Habit Inventory, to look the *reasons why* straight in the face.

And now, here is the Slim Gourmet's Food Habit Inventory, the clue to your eating personality, your weight problem—and to the smaller sizes you will soon be wearing.

THE SLIM GOURMET'S
FOOD HABIT INVENTORY
FOR

_____   _____
Name   Date

_____ _____   _____   _____
Age   Sex   Height   Profession

_____   _____
Present Weight   Highest Weight Reached

Please write down exactly what you ate and drank yesterday.
Don't omit half a peanut.

Calories
(_Don't write in
this space now!_)

BREAKFAST		
BETWEEN BREAKFAST AND LUNCH		
LUNCH		
BETWEEN LUNCH AND DINNER		
DINNER		
DURING THE EVENING		

EXACT ANSWERING OF THESE QUESTIONS WILL *HELP YOU*

1. Which meals do you eat regularly?
   breakfast_____ mid-morning snack_____ lunch_____
   afternoon tea, coffee or other snack_____ dinner_____ late
   snack_____
2. Which of these is the most important meal?_____
3. Which is the least important meal?_____
4. (For housewives!) Do you eat or taste much when preparing
   meals? yes_____ no_____
5. How many courses has your main meal? one_____ two_____
   three_____ more_____
6. Do you like a sweet dessert? yes_____ no_____
7. What do you drink regularly with your meals? water_____
   milk_____ tea or coffee_____ alcoholic beverages_____
   non-alcoholic beverages_____
8. How often do you eat in restaurants during a normal week
   in your home town? _____ times per week
9. Do you have your lunch—at home?_____ at your office?_____
   in restaurant?_____ at a club?_____
10. Do you have a sandwich lunch?_____ or a knife-and-fork
    lunch?_____
11. Do you eat on Sundays (week ends) more_____ or less_____
    than on weekdays?
12. What does your Sunday breakfast or brunch consist of?

    _____

    _____

13. Have you changed your eating ways during the last 3 years?
    Please answer how:

    _____

    _____

    _____

14. How many rolls or slices of bread do you eat a day?_____
15. What kind of bread do you like most? white_____ whole
    wheat_____ rye_____ Melba toast_____ other type of
    bread_____

16. What cereals do you eat regularly?_____
17. Do you like puddings?_____ pies?_____ cakes?_____
    biscuits?_____ ice cream?_____ pastries?_____
18. Do you like sweets? yes_____ no_____
19. Do you eat nuts or almonds? yes_____ no_____
20. Do you eat chocolate or other sweets between meals? yes_____
    no_____
21. What special foods do you usually eat
    1. at Christmas time?_____
    2. around Easter?_____
    3. on your birthday?_____
22. What dishes did your mother prepare especially well?_____
    _____
    _____

23. What cheeses do you eat?_____
    _____

24. Please name the 2 foods or dishes you like most_____
    _____

25. Please name the 2 foods or dishes you dislike most_____
    _____

26. What do you dislike so strongly that you refuse it when offered?
    _____

27. Name 2 seasonings you use most: salt_____ pepper_____
    mayonnaise_____ mustard_____ ketchup_____ chili sauce_____
28. What do you drink? soft drinks_____ hard liquor_____
    wine_____ water_____ beer_____ milk_____ skimmed
    milk_____ buttermilk_____
29. Are you a "social drinker" only?_____ or do you also drink
    when you are alone?_____
30. Do you drink when you feel tense?_____
31. Do you drink your tea or coffee with cream?_____ with
    sugar?_____ with both?_____ without anything?_____
32. How many cups of coffee and/or tea do you average a day?_____
33. Do you have a bar at home? yes_____ no_____
34. If yes, would you please list what is in your bar at this moment?
    _____

35. Does coffee interfere with your sleep? yes_____ no_____
36. What do you smoke? cigarettes_____ cigars_____ pipe_____
    not at all_____

37. Do you smoke during the meal, between courses? yes_____ no_____

38. When sad, disappointed, furious, or depressed, does your appetite disappear?_____ or increase?_____

39. Do you usually take second helping? yes_____ no_____

40. If you take second helpings, do you do so because you like the dish?_____ or to be polite to host or hostess?_____or out of habit?_____

41. Do you leave food on your plate? yes_____ no_____

42. Do you order what you like most in restaurants?_____ or what you cannot get at home?_____

43. Would you like restaurant portions larger?_____ smaller?_____ as they are?_____

44. Which foods did you miss most when you dieted last?_____
_____
_____

45. Please note all meats that come to your mind in one minute:
_____
_____
_____

46. Please note all vegetables that come to your mind in one minute:_____
_____
_____

(FOR THE WOMAN OF THE HOUSE ONLY)

47. Do you consider yourself a good_____ average_____ poor_____ cook?

48. How often do you buy food during the week? once_____ twice_____ daily_____

49. Who gets the biggest portions in your household?_____

50. Who gets the choice pieces of the food you serve?_____

51. Who eats the leftovers?_____

52. Do you use leftovers economically?_____

53. Are you as good_____ or not so good_____ a cook as your mother? As good_____ not so good_____ as your husband's mother?

54. If you have children, do they eat the same meals as their parents? yes_____ no_____ or do you prepare for your husband special dishes the children do *not* get? yes_____ no_____

11 TWENTY-ONE REASONS

WHY PEOPLE GAIN WEIGHT

My congratulations! You have just taken a long step toward the permanent end of your overweight. You now know more about your food character than you ever knew before. Probably you have never before asked yourself so many questions and brought so many hidden facts about your eating into the daylight.

The next step is to evaluate these answers and use them in your search for the *reasons why* you have gained weight in the past. These will lead you to the *ways how* to live yourself into a new food philosophy and lose the surplus pounds almost automatically.

If you plan to consult a doctor, this is the moment to do it. You can take along this book with your answers to the Food Habit Inventory and discuss with him the Slim Gourmet's way to reduce as it best applies to you. You might ask him:

Is my metabolism normal? Can my digestive system manage all kinds of foods? If not, which foods should I exclude? Do you agree that I should reduce on a daily deficit of 500 calories? At what weight should I stop reducing?

This visit to the doctor is not only wise but essential for those readers who know that they have a health problem in addition to their overweight, such as a glandular deficiency, metabolism that is not within the normal range, peptic ulcer, or any digestive disturbance.

If you are one of the ninety-nine out of a hundred light or heavy overweights who are otherwise in normal health and whose excess pounds are the result of overeating through the years, we can go on to the next step. As you saw, there was a column in the Inventory in which you were asked not to write at once. It was reserved for the calories you spent on that one day's meals that you listed, as I hope, conscientiously and honestly.

Calories are a convenient measure by which we count our food requirements. (Actually they measure the fuel or energy value of food.) In Chapter Eight you found your daily calorie maintenance allowance—that is, the number of calories a person of your size, sex, and activity needs each day to maintain your ideal weight. At the back of this book you will find a reliable calorie guide that shows you how many calories were contained in the foods you ate on your sample day.

Do the best you can to remember the sizes of the portions you ate. A single hamburger can be anything from 100 to 500 calories, so it is obviously important to size up your portions. (Look back at Chapter Nine for average portion sizes.)

Now fill in the calories for your sample day and add up the total. You can see at a glance whether on that day you remained within the daily calorie maintenance allowance you have set for yourself, or exceeded it, and whether you overate a great deal or only a little.

To give an example: if your calorie maintenance allowance is 2,000 a day, and you find that on your sample day your eating amounted to 2,800 calories, it is clear that you are a heavy overeater, and you have already found the general cause of your overweight (but you have still to find the reasons why you are overeating so heavily).

On the other hand, don't be too quick to rejoice if your addition shows that you took only 2,000 calories on that day, or even a little less. There may be two reasons for this: (1) that you have cheated yourself by not remembering everything you ate; (2) that while you remembered everything, on just this day you happened to eat moderately. There may be other days in the week when you add to your weight by overeating. Most people, for instance, eat more in general, and particularly more snacks, during the week end than on weekdays. If you chose a weekday for your sample, you might check yourself by noting down also your record for a Saturday or Sunday. Make a rough average now; you will look into your week-end eating more carefully when we come to Chapter Thirteen.

This is the moment to reread your Food Habit Inventory. Read it as if you were a doctor reading the case history of a new patient. Take a pencil and wherever you find a food habit that you believe is unique and unlike the habits of other people you know, make a mark. As you pick out the ways in which you appear to differ from your family and friends and neighbors, your own special, individual food personality will become clearer to you, especially in those small details to which until now, perhaps, you paid no attention. These may be the very clues you are seeking to the causes of your overweight and the ways by which you will lose it.

You are going to take a very objective look at this newly revealed food personality of yours. I recommend that you do not continue your research any further today, but let a day or two pass before you begin to follow up the clues to your overweight. From a little distance you can see the picture more clearly.

So place a bookmark at this point and close the book for today. Tomorrow or the next night, set aside two quiet hours for a second consultation with yourself, when you will seek out the reasons why and the ways how—in other words, your own Slim Gourmet philosophy.

To Be Read One or Two Days Later

For most people, as we know, the cause of overweight is overeating (and the cause of even considerable overweight may be only a little overeating through the years). Eating has different meanings for different people, and overeating, a little or a lot, has its own explanations for each of us. Each of us also does his overeating in his own ways: some of us do it with snacks, some with soft or strong drinks, and most of us overeat in more ways than one. To help you in your search for your own, out of the many possible causes for overweight, the twenty-one most common ones are listed here in three groups.

It is your job to choose the three main *whys* of your overweight. Whether you find them on this list or have some unique ones of your own, they will be your guideposts to the way you will go in your reducing. You will discover in these pages how you can eliminate, one after the other, your own principal causes for gaining weight, and thus reduce safely and agreeably to the point where you are happy, healthy, and comfortable with your weight.

I have known overweight people to whom all twenty-one of the reasons listed here apply. But usually a few lead the rest. If we can eliminate those more important causes of overweight we have already done a big job.

So let's begin the job and concentrate at first on the obvious: (1) Select your three main *whys*; (2) arrange them in order of importance, and (3) begin to think about how you can eliminate them, one by one.

TWENTY-ONE REASONS WHY

BIOLOGICAL	1.	Faulty metabolism
MEDICAL	2.	Glandular disturbances

PSYCHOLOGICAL	3.	Worry
	4.	Inner unrest
	5.	Feelings of failure
	6.	Boredom and loneliness
	7.	Inability to say "no"

HABITUAL	8.	Absence of mind when eating
	9.	Lack of food knowledge
	10.	Monotonous menus

11. Poorly organized menus
12. Limited food vocabulary
13. Too large portions
14. Too many forbidden foods
15. Too much liquid
16. Food superstitions
17. Scavenger-eating
18. Imitative eating
19. Reliance on drugs
20. Week-end eating
21. Uninteresting cooking

These *whys* are discussed in one form or another in the various chapters of this book. To speed your search, let us recapitulate them briefly here.

Reasons 1 and 2, the biological and medical causes of overweight which, as we know, apply only to a very small percentage of overweight people, can be dealt with only by the medical profession. If you know that your metabolism functions abnormally or that you have a glandular disturbance, I recommend that you follow the Slim Gourmet's philosophy only after your physician has selected and approved those sections that apply to you.

We come now to the psychological *whys*:

3. *Worry as a Reason Why.* In the not so distant past when food was scarce, especially at certain seasons, our ancestors ate like squirrels. They stuffed when food was plentiful and starved when it was not. In times of anxiety or worry we seem to revert to this practice. Before an examination, a meeting, or a decision on which much depends, at a time when one feels anything but safe in his shoes, almost everyone eats more than usual and without exercising much choice. We eat at such periods not only to satisfy the appetite but also for the comfort of a well-filled stomach which for the moment quiets our anxiety.

4. *Inner Unrest as a Reason Why.* To many people, eating is a medicine against unrestful feelings. This reason is not far dif-

ferent from the foregoing one, but there are people who are restless not only at specific anxious times but all their lives. They eat almost without knowing it, frequently in bits and pieces. They look forward to a meal as the only time during the day when their tensions relax.

5. *Feelings of Failure as a Reason Why.* Children who are doing poorly at school, adults who do not have the success they want, people of any age who are inwardly dissatisfied with their achievement, frequently tend to seek solace for feelings that have been hurt in the outside world by overeating at the family table. A big wedge of pie or a rich sundae is often a poultice to a wounded ego.

6. *Boredom and Loneliness as a Reason Why.* Boredom, lack of occupation, is a frequent *why* among adults; loneliness leads many children to become overweight. They make up for the love that is missing or that they believe to be missing from their environment by overeating, secret eating, and often a special craving for sweets.

7. *Inability to Say "No" as a Reason Why.* It is always easier to say "yes" than "no." Our social habits make it very difficult to refuse graciously offered drinks or food. Custom has taught us that refreshment must be offered and consumed continuously when we entertain or are being entertained. At the family table, not eating, or refusing a second helping, is frequently considered an insult to the cook, and when Mother is the cook there is almost no escape from paying her the compliment of overeating. Eating long after the appetite has been satisfied is often a consequence of the inability to say "no."

Of the psychological *whys* it is often said that they are unconscious, and that is true. But it is also true, I have discovered, that our *habitual* reasons for overeating can be, and often are, equally unconscious. Our overeating itself is usually a practice of which we are unaware. And that is why we are working so hard at this moment. We are trying to become conscious of all our reasons for overeating and gaining weight, because only when we are conscious of them can we deal with them. So now let us continue with the habitual *whys:*

8. *Absence of Mind When Eating as a Reason Why.* The Slim Gourmet's philosophy teaches: "Eat with all your senses." How can you do that when you read a newspaper at breakfast and heatedly discuss your business over lunch? Of course you eat at the same time, but do you know what you are eating? Do you know how much you are eating? Do you enjoy what you are eating? No good can come of such eating habits.

9. *Lack of Food Knowledge as a Reason Why.* Do you know what constitutes a balanced meal? Do you eat differently from the way you ate when you were a child? Do you buy a variety of foods when you go marketing? Have you a basic idea of the meaning of healthful nutrition? Do you know fairly clearly which foods please you and which do not? If you can answer all of these questions in the affirmative, this is not your reason why.

10. *Monotonous Menus as a Reason Why.* I know a man who for more than forty years has eaten the same breakfast and the same lunch and the same dinner every day of the week. For this man the enjoyment of food means only larger portions. He knows the taste of his restricted diet so well that only eating in quantity can satisfy him. The fact that he is overweight is obvious. The fact that he has also been divorced three times speaks for the superior eating habits of three women.

11. *Badly Organized Menus as a Reason Why.* The composition of a menu is an art though not a difficult one. Many people combine all rich or all lean or merely boring dishes for a meal. Many also know too little about the caloric values of various foods, and this results frequently in overeating even when the portions are small.

12. *Limited Food Vocabulary as a Reason Why.* There is an old German proverb: "What the peasant doesn't know he doesn't eat." Even in this country today there are still more people whose food vocabulary is limited to twenty or thirty dishes than there are people who make use of the rich choice

our markets offer. Do you know that American orchards produce a hundred kinds of different-looking and different-tasting apples, that there are more than sixty varieties of cheeses, that you can prepare a chicken in a hundred different ways? Even if you are aware of these facts, do you make use of them? The enlargement of your food vocabulary is a necessary step toward becoming a Slim Gourmet. Once you begin to enjoy some of the many thousands of different tastes available to you in foods, you can make *quality-eating* a weapon in your fight against *quantity-eating*.

13. *Too Large a Portion as a Reason Why*. Everybody has an ideal portion size. This size is not the same for a five-foot, two-inch woman as for her six-foot husband. The husband may need 3,500 calories a day and she only 2,000. If she eats the same steaks, the same omelets, the same ham and egg portions as he does, she is now looking her main *reason why* straight in the face.

14. *Too Many Forbidden Foods as a Reason Why*. Even foods that are not too much desired become desirable if forbidden. If a food is forbidden for a long time, we develop such a strong demand for it that once we get it we eat too much of it. If any such forbidden foods narrow your eating choices, you may develop a craving for big quantities, and this can become a *reason why*.

15. *Too Much Liquid as a Reason Why*. A bottle of Coca-Cola contains 100 calories, as many as a fair-sized roll. A whisky equals a slice of bread, a glass of orange juice counts the same as a large potato. Excepting only pure water, whatever we drink adds to our calorie intake. Frequently we neglect to include the liquids in our counting, the many cups of tea and coffee with sugar or cream or both. Have you ever kept count of how many drinks you absent-mindedly consume during a long evening? Here may be one of your important *reasons why*.

16. *Food Superstitions as a Reason Why*. "Eat another apple. Apples aren't fattening." And then you eat three apples and don't realize that this may equal a steak. But steaks are not fat-

tening either! Cottage cheese is not fattening, neither is Ry-Krisp. So many words, so many errors. Everything has a caloric value and one can also eat too much of low-calorie foods. There are no foods that are not "fattening" if eaten in excess. I have seen many overweights who gained their weight by eating only "non-fattening foods."

17. *Scavenger-Eating as a Reason Why.* "Finish what's on your plate," said the mother, and then she wondered why the child became overweight. Mother herself does not like leftovers. She therefore eats what remains on the platter. She also wonders why she weighs more and more. Scavenger-eating is a deep-rooted habit that begins usually in childhood with the thrifty admonition, "Finish what's on your plate." There is no harm in finishing if there was not too much on the plate in the first place, but scavenger-eaters finish regardless.

18. *Imitative Eating as a Reason Why.* Many of our eating habits are acquired by imitation. Children imitate what they see their parents eat, parents imitate what they saw *their* parents eat, and so our eating ways may go back to times when neither the automobile nor the electric appliance saved exercise and the spending of bodily energy. Do you eat according to the times in which you live or according to some other way of life long forgotten?

19. *Reliance on Drugs as a Reason Why.* Thyroid pills, laxatives, and the often-used and misused benzedrine keep many people living under the illusion that they can eat any quantity and still lose weight. Trust in drugs not infrequently leads to gaining weight instead of losing it. I lost eighty-two pounds in fifteen months without ever using one single pill. I find it more efficient to rely on myself than on artificial means.

20. *Week-end Eating as a Reason Why.* To overeat on Christmas or Thanksgiving is practically an American tradition. Overeating on week ends is fast becoming a general pattern. On Saturday and Sunday it is not unusual to eat twice what we eat

on any other day of the week. Must we give up our week-end pleasures? Not necessarily. The Slim Gourmet has ways to enjoy week-end leisure eating and still lose weight. But it is important to know if this is one of the *whys* of your overweight.

21. *Uninteresting Cooking as a Reason Why.* This is becoming increasingly rare. American cooking has greatly improved in homes and restaurants during the past twenty years, but there are still homes and eating places that have not kept pace. Fatty cooking, overcooking, and the indiscriminate use of ketchup are enemies of enjoyable eating. If the dish is cooked without regard to taste and appetizing appearance, we lose our interest in it. Eating becomes a mechanical duty. We eat too fast—and too much.

This completes the twenty-one most common *whys* of overweight. Are you having trouble selecting the three principal ones for your own extra pounds? Naturally, there are likely to be more than three for you, as there were for me and are for almost everyone. But nature is basically simple: so many surplus calories, so many surplus pounds. It is living that is complicated, and the complexities of our lives frequently prevent us from seeing the obvious causes of our difficulties.

So let us simplify. Let us attack first causes first. The more subtle secondary ones can be dealt with later.

Here are some hints to help you choose your three main *whys,* and then to check whether you are right.

Suppose, for instance, that you suspect week-end eating is your principal difficulty. This is so generally true that although we have mentioned it before and will go into it thoroughly in a later chapter, we can check it quickly here. Take the record of what you ate on one Saturday or Sunday (perhaps you have already made a record, to check the calorie count of your sample day). Add up separately the calories for this and compare them with the total for your sample day. If your weekday comes to 2,000 calories and your Sunday costs you 3,000 you have only to multiply your Sunday surplus of 1,000 calories by fifty-two, and you know why last year you gained the fifteen pounds that irk you now.

There are a number of key questions in the Inventory. Questions 45 and 46 give you the clue to *Reason Why* number 12. How many kinds of meats and meat dishes did you know? Fewer than ten? Then your food vocabulary can stand enlargement. Did you know more than thirty meat dishes, or vegetables? Then you have no worry about your food vocabulary. There must be other causes for your overweight.

What was your answer to Question 40, which asked you whether you take second helpings because you like to eat more or to be polite? If politeness is your answer, then one of your main *whys* may be number 7, the Inability to Say "No."

After reading your Food Habit Inventory again you may be in doubt whether you chose the right *whys* for you, or placed them in the right order. Don't hesitate to change. Don't hesitate to take the time you need to be content with your choices. It is important that you yourself feel satisfied with your analysis, and especially with the selection of the THREE MOST IMPORTANT REASONS WHY YOU GAINED WEIGHT.

From now on we are going to concentrate on eliminating your overweight by eliminating the causes of it, beginning with these three and attending to them in order, one at a time. We do not expect to accomplish this overnight. It takes a little time and patience, a little good humor, and above all it takes new knowledge and adventure into the joys of eating to reduce in the Slim Gourmet's way, succcessfully, comfortably, and for all time.

12   THE FORTY-FIVE

WEEKLY HABIT-TESTERS

I have met many candidates for the Slim Gourmet's way who have had difficulty changing the food habits that are troublesome to them. Even the very honest answering of all the questions of the Food Habit Inventory does not give them sufficient information on the comparative strength of their habits. They need a way to find out which habits are so deeply ingrained that they cannot be changed, and which can be changed relatively easily.

When I was a stout gourmet, trying to free myself from eating habits that had made me gain weight, in order to become better acquainted with myself I worked out a system of habit-testing. I chose one habit at a time, and for a week—and a week only—I gave up that particular habit and observed how I got along without it.

For example, if you think you cannot drink coffee without cream, just for a week try to do so. If you discover that after the first two or three days you are developing a liking and a taste for black coffee, taking cream in your coffee is, for you, a habit easy to change. If on the other hand you find at the end of the seventh day that you are longing to have cream again with your coffee, you must note down that this is a habit not easy for you to change. No harm is done. By the same experimental method you will come across some other calorie-high habit that you *can* change.

There are no bad habits or good ones, as I learned at the dinner party of a Bedouin sheik, when with my own ears I heard the Arab guests thank their host with a forceful belch. For those who are reducing the Slim Gourmet's way, there are habits

that are easy and comfortable to change as well as those that
are not, and we have only to find out which we can eliminate,
which we can moderate, and which we must accommodate
within our philosophy of reducing with pleasure.

I have never understood why most diet-prescribers insist upon
black coffee and at the same time allow butter on the toast. The
other way round is easier for me and saves many more calories.

Mrs. B. in Hartford, Connecticut, has done well for more than
ten years without any dinner. I could not do that, but I do work
best on the lightest of lunches. This I did not know until I
tested my habits. Until then I had always fancied that three
courses were my luncheon minimum.

Habit-testing—one habit a week—is not asking too much of
human endurance. For a week we can do without the cake or the
cocktail that has its sacred place in our way of life. When we
know that it is only for a week and for a scientific experiment, we
will endure even a little hardship, if only to write down after the
test: "No, the cocktail habit is too important to me to be
changed."

Run your eye down the Slim Gourmet's list of Forty-five
Weekly Habit-testers at the end of the chapter—perhaps you can
add some of your own—and select the twenty or thirty habits
you want to test. Choose, to begin with, a habit that seems the
least necessary to you and therefore the easiest to change. It
is always better to go from success to success. At the end of the
week write down your report on the habit you have tested, and
choose the next easiest for the next test. Thus you go from the
easy to the more difficult until you reach the point where you
abstain for a week—and only a week—from what seems the
most difficult habit to part with. For only a week, a Californian
can do without oranges or a Kentucky horse-trainer without
bourbon.

At the end of your habit-testing experiment you should have
an exact record of the depth of your habit roots.

My test comprised twenty-six habits altogether. At the end I knew that some quite substantial weight-building habits could be changed without much strain or effort. My way was clear and my conscience lightened. I could afford the pre-prandial Scotch (70 calories) and painlessly give up second helpings (saving 200 calories a day). I developed a liking for the one-course luncheon (saving 200 calories a day) and eliminated the second egg at breakfast (saving 70 calories a day).

But not for anything would I have given up my nighttime snack or the bread with dinner. These habits, when put to the test, proved to be very deeply rooted indeed.

I have had many friendly warnings from the diet experts among my friends. "Drinks don't go with a slimming diet—" "Three meals a day and no more are a must for you—" "Don't you know bread is fattening?"

I did not argue. I knew better—and I knew myself. I had the scientific proof.

That is one of the secret blessings of a conscientious program of habit-testing. You become acquainted with what you can do and what you cannot and you win an eating security that makes your reducing a pleasure, as easy as breathing.

(And here is another secret blessing: each test reduces your calorie consumption by 1,000 to 2,000 calories during the week of testing. In my case, through testing alone, I lost more than nine pounds during habit-testing time.)

HERE ARE THE SLIM GOURMET'S FORTY-FIVE WEEKLY HABIT-TESTERS

1. No strong drinks
2. No long drinks
3. No soft drinks
4. No cream in coffee
5. No sugar in tea
6. No butter on bread
7. No food after dinner
8. No drink after dinner
9. No food between lunch and dinner
10. No drinks before dinner
11. No drinks with dinner
12. No drinks before lunch
13. No drinks with lunch
14. No sauces with lunch
15. No sauces with dinner

16. No bread at breakfast
17. No bread at lunch
18. No bread at dinner
19. No bread after dinner
20. No dessert at lunch
21. No dessert at dinner
22. No sweets before dinner
23. No sweets after dinner
24. No sugar in anything
25. No dressing with salads
26. No potatoes with lunch
27. No potatoes with dinner
28. No honey or jam
29. No eggs for breakfast
30. No bacon with breakfast
31. No fruit juices after breakfast
32. No second helpings
33. No icebox raids at night
34. No ice cream or sundaes
35. No cheese
36. No larger meat portion than ½ the usual
37. No vegetable that is not "natural"
38. No fruit that is not "natural"
39. ½ the usual milk
40. Minimum breakfast:
    coffee or tea without cream and sugar
    ½ glass orange juice
    1 toast with butter
41. Minimum luncheon:
    1 toast without butter
    Lean ham, cheese, or roast beef
    1 portion fresh fruit
42. Minimum dinner:
    1 glass milk or buttermilk
    Portion of fresh fruit
    1 slice bread with boiled egg
    1 slice cheese, tongue, or meat
43. Nothing fried
44. No thick soup
45. No TV snacks

13 THE WEEK IS THE UNIT,

NOT THE DAY

Susan G. is a young, gay, pretty secretary. The only cloud in her azure sky is her plumpness. Starvation diets have been no help to her. When we assembled her food habit inventory we discovered an astonishing fact: from Monday to Friday Susan's eating added up to a modest 7,000 calories, but for Saturday and Sunday her total was 8,000 calories.

One exceptional week end could not be significant. But when a second week and a third repeated the same story, there was no doubt that Susan was eating more on the two days of the week end than in all the rest of the week put together. It was through Susan's experience that I discovered we must measure our eating by the week, not the day.

How does a smart and otherwise sensible girl develop such an unbalanced kind of eating? Very simply. The weekday breakfast is a clock-watching, am-I-going-to-be-late affair. A heavy work schedule leaves no time to think of mid-morning snacks. The kidding of her colleagues, her personal economics, time needed for errands or a walk or window-shopping, all encourage a quick inexpensive drugstore lunch without dessert (although afternoon hunger and fatigue make her compensate guiltily with a chocolate bar). Evenings find her rushing through dinner to dress for a date.

The week end reveals a changed Susan. She is free of the tyrannizing clock. Mom is a wonderful cook and bakes a legion of cakes and pies. The house is always full of company. Pretty Susan is much dated and the boys like to take her to good eating places. Sunday breakfast is a family occasion, the only morning when all the family sits down together with leisure to talk, read the paper, gossip. One feels warm, secure, at the breakfast table. And the waffles are delicious. So is lunch; so is dinner. Here is how it added up on one of Susan's typical workdays and on any ordinary Sunday:

WEEKDAY			(Calories)	SUNDAY
Breakfast	½ grapefruit	50	50	½ grapefruit
	1 cup black coffee	0	900	3 waffles with syrup
			120	1 muffin
			50	with butter
			0	1 cup black coffee
Morning Snack	none		420	12 Brazil nuts
Luncheon	1 egg salad		250	clam chowder
	sandwich	350	300	Southern fried chicken
	1 cup black coffee	0	200	with French fries
			460	apple pie à la mode
			250	10-oz. glass of cider
Afternoon Snack	1 chocolate bar	400	430	2 doughnuts
			170	1 toast with butter and jam
			0	1 cup black coffee
Dinner	2 hamburgers with vegetables		300	canned salmon with mayonnaise
	and potatoes	500	400	breaded veal cutlets
	1 fruit cup	100	250	baked Idaho potato with 2 pats of butter
			450	peach pie à la mode
			500	2 10-oz. glasses of cider
TOTAL		1,400	5,500	

Susan was eating at the rate of 15,000 calories a week, when 14,000 (or 2,000 a day) were all she needed for her size. With her 1,000 extra calories a week, fifty-two weeks in the year, she was overeating to the tune of 52,000 calories, enough to gain fifteen pounds every twelve months. No wonder Susan was worried about her plumpness. And she needed only one look at her comparative menus, weekday and Sunday, to know exactly where she was getting those 1,000 extra calories.

And yet, isn't there a familiar sound to Susan's menus?

Doesn't it make you wonder about your own week-end eating? Make a test: write down as nearly as you can remember what you eat on a normal weekday, and what you ate—and drank— last Sunday. Do your comparative menus bear some resemblance to Susan's? To make an accurate test, write down every day's eating for two weeks, and then add up separately the calorie count for Monday through Friday and for Saturday and Sunday. If the ratio is five to two—five for the weekdays and two for the week end —you are the exception who has no week-end problem. But the chances are that you are a member in good standing of the Week-end Eating Society which apparently has active chapters from Coast to Coast.

Most people weigh three pounds more on Monday than on Thursday. Some people have other heavyweight days. Mrs. M. of Connecticut reports that hers is Wednesday, following the Tuesday bridge which means not only a good game but also three cups of tea, two glasses of soft drinks, plus candy and cookies and sandwiches and a "bridgers' competition dinner." The total is 2,000 calories from four to nine P.M.

Dr. R. eats more when he is called to attend a patient during the night. He cannot go back to sleep after the visit if he does not relieve his tension with a glass of beer and a substantial sandwich.

But for most people Saturday and Sunday are the weight-making days. Susan's week-end eating is far from unique. My own eating reaches its peak on week ends. Everyone whom I have asked has confirmed the week-end story: the Wall Street lawyer develops an enormous appetite with thirty-six holes of golf; the youthful Philadelphia grandmother enjoys the week-end visits of her children and their families; the advertising executive begins his week-end relaxation in suburban Connecticut with cocktails before lunch; the Chicago architect is an ardent amateur cook and delights in cooking for his friends on the week end. All these people live rather frugally during the working week and enjoy to the hilt their freedom from time and work pressures during their two days of leisure. For all of these whom I have mentioned, the relaxed eating and drinking of the week end has led to overweight.

Have you discovered that the week end is your Achilles' heel? And are you already resolving to keep to your 1,200- or 1,400- or 1,800-calorie limit on Saturday and Sunday as well as on weekdays? Are you setting out to shrink your Sunday breakfast, abolish your TV snacks, refuse the canapés at cocktail parties, and generally castigate yourself for daring to relax your vigilance on the week ends? Wait. Don't tamper too radically with a deep-rooted custom.

We need our week ends. We need our relaxed hours around the family table and with friends. We need to indulge in that little extra eating and drinking that differentiate the leisure days from the press and hurry of the week.

The Bible story of the Creation is our first authority for considering the Sabbath different from the other days of the week. The difference has not vanished since Old Testament days; rather, it has increased. With the American five and one-half or five-day working week we have multiplied our leisure by two.

It is natural to eat more on week ends. Our very pursuits invite more eating and drinking. Sports make us hungry. Most week ends see us in the role either of host or guest and in both we eat and drink congenially. There are—and should be—empty, lazy week-end hours, and during these we feel more like eating, and feel like it more frequently, than when we are working. The nuts, sweets, cookies are within easy reach, and the full refrigerator is just a few steps away.

For many generations Sunday breakfast and especially Sunday dinner have stood for the warming home fire and the closeness of the clan. Today many homes serve Sunday breakfast and Sunday dinner on Saturday, too, as well as twice the former number of Sunday teas, cocktails, and snacks.

Must we give up all this? Many have tried. They have held grimly to their 1,200-calorie, three-meals-a-day diet through week ends as well as weekdays. But their sufferings create so strong a pent-up demand that when the diet is over they can hardly follow even rational food habits.

Week-end eating and drinking are part of the pattern of real people living real lives. Sunday is a special day for all of us. And the Tuesday for Mrs. A. and her bridge companions, the Wednesday for Mr. J. who goes bowling, and almost any busy night in the week for Dr. R. None of these patterns fits the dieter's ideal of three meals a day and the same number of calories every day of the week. But the dieter's ideal is good only on paper.

The *daily* calorie allowance is a mathematical device. It is no more real than the concept of the average man. Just as the average man is created by statisticians for measuring purposes, the daily calorie allowance is created by dietitians for purposes of computing. It is handy, but it is not a commandment to be followed in daily living.

In real life one day is not always like another, but we do follow more or less a weekly pattern. The week is the unit of our living, not the day. Here is the weekly pattern of my friend F.:

	Before he learned the Slim Gourmet way	During his reducing year	and now
Monday	2,400 calories	1,700 calories	1,900 calories
Tuesday	2,400	1,700	2,100
Wednesday	2,600	1,700	2,200
Thursday	2,900	1,900	2,500
Friday	2,900	2,100	2,800
Saturday	3,100	2,400	2,800
Sunday	3,200	2,500	3,200
WEEK	19,500	14,000	17,500

F. overate at the rate of 2,000 calories a week. He lost a pound a week for nine months—thirty-nine pounds—by spending 3,500 calories less than his weekly calorie maintenance allowance of

17,500. Now he keeps his new slimness by staying within the 17,500 calories on which he maintains his normal weight.

But look how he does it! The same 2,500 calories every day would be quite difficult for a man of his habits. He has heavy social engagements from Thursday to Sunday, golf-playing week ends at the country club, and a giant brunch every Sunday at home. So he custom-tailored his calorie spending for the week, assigning to each day its individual allotment. Thus even while he was reducing his Sunday was not made miserable by a ready-to-wear 1,000-calorie diet which would have killed the joy of the whole family at the brunch table. His Saturday golf continued to include the genial refreshment that was part of its pleasure. And on Friday evening he could accept any invitation without sending chills down his hostess's spine by the warning, "I'm on a diet."

And when, despite all charting, the 1,900 calories for Thursday were once topped by an unbudgeted drink or an extra-sized portion of dessert, and he was overdrawn by 100 or 200 calories, it was easy for him to finance the deficit out of the more generous allowance between Friday and Sunday, and break even at the end of the week.

A wise member of one of New York's famous gourmet clubs saves calories at luncheon when a great dinner is planned for the evening. I myself save on Monday and Tuesday for Wednesday's canasta, when good fare is as important as good cards.

The week is the unit, not the day. The midweek evening out, the week end's relaxations, need not add to our weight or our guilt, nor need their pleasures be spoiled, if we think of our eating by the week instead of the day.

In case the reader is concerned for Susan, with whom we began our week-end story, here is her happy ending. Shocked by what her food habit inventory revealed, Susan had no trouble dealing with the danger once she knew what it was. She changed her snack from nuts to fruit, established a smaller PPS for herself, eliminated second helpings, and so was able to continue enjoying all the good foods Mom's generous table offered. She settled for one rich dessert ("Does *anybody* really need pie à la mode twice a day, even on Sunday?" asked Susan) and took her afternoon coffee with one doughnut.

Her weekday eating was, of course, austere, so that with only moderate revision of her week-end eating she still had ample margin for Saturday and Sunday enjoyment, even while she transformed her weekly 1,000-calorie excess into a 1,000-calorie deficit. She began to lose pounds instead of gaining them. At last report she had shed nine pounds and was enjoying her week-end eating all the more because she ate with good conscience, without fear of the day of reckoning when she would have to go on another hunger diet and give up her Saturday and Sunday relaxation altogether. Susan will not have to diet again.

If your week ends are relaxed and happy eating times, don't destroy them. Treasure them. And plan for them. If your daily maintenance allowance is 2,500 calories, that does not mean you must spend 2,500 calories for your eating, no more, no less, every day. Arrange them by the week, as did F., to suit your week's activities. Or, if you are reducing on a daily 1,600 calories —11,200 calories weekly—you can have your pleasant week end and still reduce, like this:

Monday	— 1,200 calories	Thursday	— 1,500 calories
Tuesday	— 1,300	Friday	— 1,600
Wednesday	— 1,400	Saturday	— 2,000
	Sunday	— 2,200 calories	

This schedule may seem harder to count but it is certainly easier to keep. It conforms with our habits, and our habits are our guide to successful reducing. Our habits tell us what we need for our *total* comfort and well-being. Fighting them doesn't work, as Susan and I and most dieters have learned.

With the week as our unit, like clever shoppers we become skillful in spending our weekly calorie budget for the best values. We can live like human beings while we reduce, and so we can keep on reducing until our target is reached.

After that, our weekly maintenance allowance—the number of calories per week on which we neither lose nor gain but maintain our normal weight—is enough. Enough? It is positively sumptuous, especially on week ends!

14   MENUS REDESIGNED

We sat at a modern ranch-house dining bar and ate a four-course dinner. We were served appetizer, soup, main dish, and dessert. It was as paradoxical as riding in a horse-drawn cab to New York's Idlewild Airport to take a D.C.7 to Paris.

Most of us still eat as if we were living in Grover Cleveland's day! The designers have changed our chairs and tables and couches, our offices and houses both outside and in, and the clothing we wear in town and in the country. They have given us new table settings and new dishes and silver and glassware, new kitchens and new appliances and utensils to use in them. The task surely does not end there. We should go on and redesign our eating as well, and bring it, too, into harmony with our changed times and environment, our contemporary needs and desires. We need interior decorators not only for the house but also for its owner.

Of the twenty-six million Americans who complain about their overweight, there must be millions whose overweight is mainly a consequence of antiquated menus. The United States, of course, eats more sanely than many foreign lands. Yet even Americans are only slowly learning how to eat for joy, health, and slimness in the twentieth century. One of the new arts that should be taught in school and home is the art of menu designing.

Redesigning our menus will not only help to abolish and to prevent overweight. It will also create new eating pleasures and taste enjoyments. It can make Americans an even happier, better-natured people than they already are.

One week end, we had two dinner invitations. The great advertising man offered us:

1. hot and cold hors d'oeuvres with the drinks;
2. shrimp cocktail on artichoke hearts;
3. turkey with stuffing, sweet potatoes with marshmallows, and all the trimmings;
4. mixed salad with Roquefort dressing;
5. an enormous pineapple pie with nuts, and
6. coffee with a variety of cakes.

The feast took place in a modern suburban dwelling with Finnish furniture and picture windows. All the picture windows and functional furniture in the world could not disguise the fact that we ate like Victorians, gobbling up some 2,000 calories apiece, which were for most of the guests a full day's calorie allowance. We were dull and sleepy conversationalists by nine thirty.

The next day another dinner had to be suffered through. It was Mimi's anniversary and we expected to see again the turkey and the trimmings and all the before-and-after food and drink that a chic suburban community regards as proper entertainment.

Mimi, however, had sat at the turkey dinner the night before and had learned from the Victorian experience. Here was Mimi's menu:

1. sherry, and natural hors d'oeuvres: raw cauliflower, cucumbers, olives, peppers, asparagus stems, with a little sauce mixed of sherry, horseradish, and cream cheese;
2. a well-mixed fresh fruit salad of pineapple and apples and garden-fresh strawberries decorated with grated peanuts and served on a bed of cold creamy rice;
3. a small, very small sirloin steak with a miniature baked potato;
4. a cup of sweet boiled Turkish coffee.

With the coffee we had mints, cigars, cigarettes, and a small dish of almonds with a few raisins.

Needless to say, my Slim Gourmet heart liked the thinking that had gone into Mimi's dinner design: the wonderful taste of the natural tidbits in the sherry sauce, blending with the sherry we drank; the smallness of the sirloin which allowed us to enjoy steak without the steak-fear that creeps down my spine whenever I am confronted with a one-pound slice of United States prime steer. At Mimi's table nobody launched into the boring diet conversation, because nobody had to apologize for not overeating. She gave us no more than the 900 calories everyone among us could eat without fear of consequences.

The most famous hotelkeeper in Berlin, Louis Adlon, used to tell the story of Ivar Kreuger, the Swedish match king who struck pay dirt in match boxes during the Twenties. The man must have suffered often and deeply from the rigors of classical French menus which were the standard of fine eating everywhere in Europe in those years.

One evening when he was alone, he ordered in his room at the plush Adlon Hotel the following dinner: first course, ice cream; second course, whipped cream mixed with pumpernickel; third course, French-fried potatoes.

The Adlons—those good guardians of the French-Prussian tradition—were shocked. So was the headwaiter. What they must have said in the kitchen could not be fit to print. But whatever else we may think of Mr. Kreuger's place in history, we must admire his dinner (if not his taste in food) as the gesture of a man of the twentieth century who knew what he wanted and refused to be intimidated by the scowl of an apoplectic Herr Ober.

Like a certain great war correspondent at the Battle of Valmy, where the world witnessed its first artillery duel, the Slim Gourmet is almost tempted to say, "From this moment we may date a new chapter in world history." Even though Mr. Kreuger's menu was too personal for us to date a new menu age from that memorable meal, it was still within the 900-calorie limit of a normal dinner.

We draw from this story one principle for menu designers: Forget what "one" serves; serve what you like and what suits a modern dining table and a modern way of life.

Your guests will like it. It need not be weird or strange. The houses we live in and the clothes we wear are not strange. Mimi's little steaks were familiar and welcome as well as delicious.

Another antiquated bogey of the dinner table is the fixed order of the menu. Hostesses, guests, restaurants, and most families monotonously have the soup follow the appetizer, the dessert follow the main dish, and the coffee come always at the end of the meal. If we apply our principle of modern menu design not only to *what* to eat but also *how* to eat, we liberate ourselves from this ponderous routine, too.

Many Americans have already changed the order bequeathed by tradition, by having their coffee served with the meal. The Dutch do this with their coffee at lunch and the Chinese with their tea at all meals. Even the tradition-bound French have lifted many of the restrictions of the old order. Nowadays they eat their pâté at the beginning instead of after the meat course.

The Slim Gourmet goes a step farther. He can design a dinner like this:

first course:	golden Delicious apple with honey
second course:	cauliflower and asparagus salad with Roquefort dressing
third course:	Virginia ham slice topped with poached egg

If tea or coffee is served with the third course he includes a slice of dry toast. The whole 700- or 800-calorie dinner will leave family and Slim Gourmet highly satisfied, provided it is well prepared and all foods are of the best quality.

Does this seem too light or too simple a dinner to you? Possibly it is. If you take a light luncheon and need more substantial fare in the evening, here is another redesigned menu. This one can be offered at a dinner party:

first course: mixed salad and State of Maine sage cheese
second course: shrimp soufflé
third course: roast beef and a baked potato "natural taste"

The right drink for such an 800-calorie dinner would be a *rosé* or red wine served with the second course. Soufflé goes well with the red wine, the shrimps notwithstanding.

At this opportunity I want to caution my readers against following too strictly the "what wine with what course" dictators. I read again and again, and hear in the houses of friends and in restaurants, that under no circumstances may you serve red wine with any kind of fish. I have the impression that these gastronomical dictators copy their decrees from one another without ever trying them out.

I recommend just once trying a shrimp soufflé with a light Beaujolais, or a heavy red Burgundy with lobster. If you can forget what you read on all those charts you will find that not only do they go very well together but that the red wine brings out a flavor in the shellfish you had not discovered before.

Go a step further and eat a trout accompanied by any red wine. If you like dry wine, try the light California red and you will discover a completely new way to enjoy trout, marrying the tangy tenderness of the fish with the fruity and non-acid taste of the wine. Wine-drinking, like eating, can also bear a little redesigning.

The roast beef at the end of our second dinner menu is the crown of the meal. It allows you to sit a little longer at the table, finishing the wine or, if you prefer, the beer served in wine glasses. In case you serve beer, water has to be served for the first two courses. The strong taste of beer would overwhelm the soufflé's subtle flavor.

Who is to be the redesigner of your menus? Nobody but yourself. There will be no design dictatorship. This will be a democratic design, in which you can choose the order of the meal, its courses and its composition, suiting entirely your own wishes when you eat alone.

When you design for company, you will of course give thought to what your company will like. Nobody will consider you a bad host or hostess when you step off the beaten path and, like a discriminating Slim Gourmet, give your guests new table delicacies and a new joy in eating. It will be a pleasure that is not paid for the next day by an uncomfortable digestive system or the necessity of starving to make up for overeating at your table.

The new menu design fights the pernicious, monotonous, health-menacing consequences of our great enemy: routine. In a city that you visit for the first time, you see and remember the street signs better than all the shops and advertising signs you see every day on your way to and from your place of work. The familiar and the routine have the same dulling effect on our eating pleasure. How many of us no longer enjoy turkey, one of the finest of our edible fowls, because we eat it too often, and always prepared the same way? Only change can make us newly aware of quality.

Menu designing for the Slim Gourmet is of course quite personal. He keeps in mind his allotment of calories to the several meals of the day. This division depends on how many meals he habitually eats, which meals he likes light, and which a little more substantial. My own appropriation of my 2,000 daily calories during reducing was: breakfast, 350 calories; luncheon, 450 calories; dinner, 900 calories; snacks and drinks, 300 calories.

This is a fairly evenly distributed order of meals. I can imagine that it might not be satisfactory to people who live in smaller cities, have shorter working hours, and can arrange their meals less freely than I do.

Another example: among my correspondents is a relatively small woman who works mainly in the evening, goes to bed late, and accordingly begins the day late. She is one of the rare people for whom three meals a day are absolutely sufficient. She has a calorie maintenance allowance of 1,900 calories, and a reducing allowance of 1,600 calories. She divides her reducing allowance like this: breakfast and lunch together, 500 calories; 6 o'clock dinner, 700 calories; 12 o'clock supper, 400 calories.

We did some menu redesigning in the case of Mrs. O., when we found that in the course of her unsuccessful attempts to diet she had for many years denied herself one of the pleasures reminiscent of her childhood in the house of her Italian parents. How could she eat spaghetti and grow thin? She had read in her many diets that spaghetti, along with potatoes and rice, was Starch Enemy Number One. Obediently she cut spaghetti from her life altogether, and limited herself to the supposedly non-fattening meat and egg dishes which are offered as the only permissible diet foods by these mass-produced diets-for-everybody.

Mrs. O., a night worker, prepared her supper when she came home from her work at about two o'clock in the morning. She allowed herself a consommé or fruit salad, four slices of cold roast beef or Virginia ham, and two or three apples, pears, or peaches. Incidentally her other meals were well balanced.

I asked her why she could not redesign her suppers a little closer to her heart's desire. She could include, every now and then, a one-dish spaghetti meal, warming and comforting as well as delicious at that late hour of the night when she must eat her supper. I told her how to prepare her spaghetti à la Slim Gourmet, in this manner: two cupfuls of spaghetti cooked *al dente,* which means not cooked too soft, mixed at the table with three pats of butter and a blend of grated old cheeses into which go old Swiss, old Dutch cheese, and old Parmesan. Mrs. O. was happy with this advice. She has continued to reduce on this meal, not eating it too often and not allowing it to become routine.

Many of us have hidden or conscious desires for foods we mistakenly shun as "fattening." This craving need not go unsatisfied.

Take the case of the daughter of a well-known professor. She is a little too heavy for her own taste and the taste of her family. Her longing is to eat a bowl of bean soup—not the harmless kind of bean soup but the heavy, sausage-studded, potato-wedded bean soup of which an average portion counts 400 calories. When bean soup was served, one winter night, and we were all enjoying a cup of its hearty warmth, I asked for the daughter of the house. She was dieting, they said. She was having a lonely egg in her room and would join us later.

Now this young lady can afford between 800 and 900 calories for her dinner. I see no reason why she should not from time to time satisfy her very personal desire for the soup that to her is divine. She can make her dinner on one bowl of her favorite, plus a salad and a fruit dessert, and stay within her allowance for dinner. She can dine on bean soup alone and nothing else, and have two bowls if she likes.

It is the unfulfilled wishes that are dangerous. Once your secret food longing is satisfied, the compulsion, the desire, the urge to have that and nothing else leaves you for a time; your eating balance is restored, and with it your peace of mind. When your wish rises demandingly again, you are again safely able to satisfy it without guilt or remorse—or extra pounds. Redesigning your menus can take care of hidden longings and protect your reducing program.

For the next dinner party you give, do a little creative menu-designing. This book gives you quite a number of hints. When you see that your guests enjoy the redesigned meal, you will gain confidence for your next redesigned menu, and you, your family, and your guests will at last be enjoying your meals in tune with the twentieth century.

Remember, too, that one out of every three Americans is weight-conscious. The same is true of your guests. Some low-calorie hors d'oeuvres among the high-calorie ones—shrimps, green olives, raw cauliflower, radishes—are much appreciated. The most delicious party dinner need count no more than 900 calories, and 700 calories make a sumptuous luncheon. Nor have you any obligation to match the portion sizes of restaurants frequented by prize fighters. The chances are a hundred to one against your having a guest who needs 5,000 calories to keep in form.

15 THE SLIM GOURMET ON THE SCALE

Once a week is weighing day, the same day each week. Thursday is the day when most people's weight is lowest. It is understood that you weigh yourself in the same clothing or, better, without any clothing at all. Those who have no weight-controller in the bathroom must be sure to visit the very same drugstore scale on the same day each week and as nearly as possible at the same time of day. Unlike the Swiss, we do not yet have government controlled scales in the United States, and different scales can differ as much as several pounds from one drugstore to another. And you must remember not only to use the same scale, but also to keep in mind from one week to the next whether you stood on the scale with or without your coat and what kind of shoes you were wearing. Also take into account changes in the weight of your clothing with the change of seasons.

There is no advantage in weighing every day. One pound a

week means less than three ounces daily and the scales are not sensitive enough to show that tiny difference. Instead of a steady mathematical loss of nine ounces in three days, your scale may even show your weight on Tuesday to be two pounds more than on Monday, and some other whimsical variation on Wednesday.

These differences in *daily* weight are of no importance. They show the normal ups and downs of the water economy of the body. If you happened to eat a very salty dish on Sunday and consequently drank a few extra glasses of water, your weight has not changed but your body may be temporarily heavier by as much as four pounds because of the retained fluid. The scale shows your total, water included. It is no precision instrument for the weight of your fatty tissue. A few days later your weight goes down with a drop of several pounds at once and that, too, is quite normal.

Weighing before and after a tennis set or an hour's horseback riding or walking on a hot day may show weight losses up to four pounds. That is not reducing but only loss of water by exertion and perspiration. The fat remains and the water must soon be restored.

The wisest way to use the scale is to make one day a week a special day for weighing. I am not sure, however, that you will follow this sensible advice any more than I did when I was reducing. Waiting a week seems more than most people have patience to do. I know very intelligent women and very serious business and professional men who each day invest a dime, penny by penny, weighing themselves on every scale they can put their feet on as they go about their day's affairs. They want so badly to see their weight go down that they must try out every scale in sight.

If you must do this, go ahead. It is an innocent game for the child that lives in each of us. It does no harm as long as you remember that the only true measure of success or failure in your reducing is your regular bathroom or drugstore scale that tells you the unadorned truth on the same day of every week.

When I was reducing, I charted my week-to-week target in my

notebook like this: May 3 198 lbs.; May 10 197 lbs.; May 17 196 lbs.; May 24 195 lbs.

And so on, until the far-off day when my ideal weight was to be reached. It gave me great satisfaction every Thursday to put a check after the target figure indicating that I had reached it. There was not one week, during the seventy-eight weeks I had to lose my unwanted pounds, that I failed to enjoy this satisfaction, once I had found the Slim Gourmet's way and had set realistic targets for myself.

There was a time before this when I thought I could do it more quickly. Why not two pounds per week? But I found, more often than I liked, that I could not always reach the target. With so many pounds to lose, so long a way to go, one disappointing week was really depressing.

One pound a week is better. It sounds like half as much success, but it is really twice as much, because when you set your target for only one pound per week you do not let a week go by without losing that pound. Week after week after week, steadily, regularly, without pain and without strain—another pound gone, and another, until all of the extra pounds are gone, and gone for good. Take the word of the Slim Gourmet: it works.

The steady, step-by-step approach to a goal by means of targets that are *within reach* is the professional secret of the successful worker in many fields. Take writing as an example. The amateur may think that if he plunges furiously into writing with the idea of producing ten pages a day, at the end of a month he will have finished a book! That book will never be written. The professional writer's daily schedule is much less ambitious, but it is feasible: perhaps no more than two pages every day, but those two pages every day without fail—that is the way to get to the end of the book. And that is the way to get to the end of your overweight. A pound a week is within the scope of the possible. Once you have mapped out your personal version of the Slim Gourmet's way, you will find it agreeable, easy, and therefore you will stick to it.

Used once a week, your scale is trustworthy. You may tell yourself that it has moods, that it is influenced by the heat or the cold, the dampness or the dryness, that the mechanism does this or that or perhaps it is the way you happened to step on it. There are dozens of fairy tales to explain away an unfavorable reading of your weight, but they are only tricks you are playing on yourself. If you are not one pound less every weighing day you must have made a mistake in your eating.

That is not fatal. You will be more careful next week. You will revise your portion-size estimates. You will reconsider whether your omelet on Wednesday counted for only 200 calories; more likely it was 300. When in doubt you will give yourself the benefit of counting more calories for the doubtful dish.

The Slim Gourmet's way is flexible. During the week you have enough opportunities to balance a day's unintentional or unplanned overeating by undereating for the next day or the next two days. You may not always keep to your target in terms of your *daily* calorie allowance. But your *weekly* calorie allowance is ironclad.

There is no need to upset your peace of mind by overstepping your weekly calorie allowance. Neither a wedding nor Thanksgiving nor a visit to New Orleans can make you deviate from your reducing program. You yourself made the program. You took your own habits, your own ways of living and eating, your own needs and wishes as a foundation. You did not ask the impossible of yourself. To make the possible come true is not more than you can do.

And the scale will dip its needle to you in salute, week after week!

16 THE SLIM GOURMET'S ART

OF SELF-DEFENSE

Our best friends are often the worst enemies of our reducing program. They worry. They tempt us to eat more. The skillful reducer needs to be skillful also in the art of self-defense.

An excellent defense, at the beginning at least, is not to advertise the fact that one is reducing. Followers of the Slim Gourmet's way, of course, have no difficulty keeping this secret. They eat and drink everything, even dessert, take their drink when it is in order, and do not forgo the pleasant snack. At table, unlike the unhappy dieter, they relish their food and joyfully share their discoveries of new taste pleasures with their companions.

They also have the defense of the United States Mint Calorie Counter. This is not only a protection against having to add and subtract in public, and thus reveal to all the fact that one is slimming. It is also a defense against forgetting how many calories we have spent, against overdrawing our calorie account, and against just not being able to add very well! It is the Slim Gourmet's secret weapon for the self-defense of reducers against attack both from without and from within. It was when I was looking for a calorie-counting device that I made this remarkable discovery: The United States Mint has produced an ideal one. Equipped with this government-tested counting device, you can count your calorie intake without benefit of pencil and paper, defend yourself against errors in arithmetic, and guard your secret even from your spouse.

This calorie counter can only be read by you. It is discreet and reliable. The cost is between $1.50 and $3.50, and your money is refunded in full when you wish to resell.

Let us assume that your reducing allowance is 1,800 calories daily. In that case your United States Mint Slim Gourmet Calorie Counter will cost you $1.80. It consists of two quarters, eight dimes, and ten nickels, preferably mint-new and gleaming. (You can get them from any bank.) That is your daily food allowance: each nickel stands for 50 calories, each dime for 100 and each quarter for 250.

This allowance is to be placed each morning in one of two special compartments of a lady's handbag or in one of two chosen pockets of a man's coat or trousers where money is not usually carried. The counting is then done in this manner: you "pay" for everything you eat or drink by taking the appropriate coin from its first compartment or pocket and placing it in the second. When the $1.80 is all gone from the first compartment into the second, then your daily calorie allowance is exhausted and you cannot go on "spending," just as you cannot go on buying when you have no money.

"But when I have no money with me I can still charge what I buy, can't I?" says the lady, and her husband points out, "I can get what I need on credit."

Of course. And in the same way, if you have very individual habits, if one day you eat less than your daily allowance and another day more, you can square your accounts with the triple calorie counter. In this instance you take your "allowance" for three days, which for a 1,800 daily allowance would be $5.40, and you spend according to your eating habits. But you had better count your remaining "capital" around the middle of the second day; otherwise you may have to forgo the third evening's dinner, and that is against the Slim Gourmet's philosophy.

For most of us the simple one-day United States Mint Calorie Counter is sufficient. I used it for more than fifteen months while reducing, and I have maintained my weight since then with its help. It is reliable and practical, and above all, it is discreet. I merely shift a quarter from one pocket into another when I eat my 250-calorie hamburger at luncheon. And a nickel for the spinach. And a dime for the mashed potatoes.

Before I sit down to dinner I can count what is left in my pocket. Nobody will notice me doing this. I know how I stand. I can eat with confidence exactly the portions that are within my calorie-means. I like to leave a dime or two when possible, as a reserve against accounting mistakes or to be "carried over" to the next day, or for an extra bite in my midnight snack if I should want it.

The United States Mint Calorie Counter confers that sense of security with which the Slim Gourmet likes to enjoy his meal. It is even more useful after reducing, for those followers of the Slim Gourmet's way who want to maintain their health and slimness. When reducing is over and you are once again living on your full 2,500 daily calorie allowance, with $2.50 in your calorie pocket you feel like a millionaire who can buy almost anything he wants to eat.

Of course, you have to know the calorie values of the foods you like. Before many weeks you will remember most of them. But you can always look them up. Calorie charts are available in pocket size at any drugstore, stationery store, or book store. And there is a precise and tested one at the back of this book.

Success in following the Slim Gourmet's way also, of course, has its hazards. The joy with which you eat, the discreetness of your United States Mint Calorie Counter, expose you to the great kindness of your host who, seeing how much you savored your first helping, presses a second on you. "Just a drumstick— otherwise my wife will think you don't like her dinner." Or, as my friend Milton used to say, "Otherwise the family will be eating turkey the rest of the week." And you (I, everybody) will blush, stammer, and accept the extra drumstick, veal bird, waffle.

Should you explain that if you do this only fifty times a year you will add ten pounds to the weight you are trying to control? Should you point out that by eating only 500 calories less than your body uses up every day you are going to lose fifteen pounds in six months—and that as he piles up your plate for the second time your host is pushing a good part of those unwanted calories back at you?

Hardly. Food and the joy of eating make good table conversation, but diets and calories do not. Besides, you will never succeed in outwitting the self-appointed consultants and well-intentioned wreckers by advertising the fact that you are reducing.

My friend G. weathers the second-helping crisis by eating so slowly that her plate is still half full when the seconds are being offered. But not everyone can eat slowly. I, for instance, am a fast eater. Often my plate is the first at the table to show its pattern. So I have invented another way. Compliments to the food can be made in words as well as in calories.

"The second never tastes as good as the first and when I've enjoyed such good food I don't dare take a second." Or, "Eating such a wonderful dish twice would be like asking Toscanini to play the symphony right over again."

Or the psychoanalytic answer: "When I was a child my parents never allowed us to have a second helping." The analysts have educated us to have such respect for childhood experiences that this disclosure usually wins sympathy and a reprieve from the second helping.

Sometimes there is no escape. Our hosts and hostesses are kind, friendly people. They mean no harm. They are only showing what was considered warm hospitality in another century. Perhaps, to make your host comfortable, you must take a second helping of something—a harmless something like three stalks of asparagus or one broccoli spear, half a spoonful of peas, a little salad.

What if your host heaps your plate too generously at the start, and your parents trained you to eat to the last crumb on your plate? This early *waste not, want not* education puts extra pounds on many of us, and it can defeat the best-planned reducing program. In my own case, the teaching of thrifty parents made a dinner-mare of a too generously piled plate. But I have learned to eat my personal-portion-sized share and leave the rest. After all, I have reasoned, self-destruction cannot be the aim of good manners!

Thus the follower of the Slim Gourmet's way, defending himself with ease and grace, progresses on his joyful path—until the day arrives when the success of his reducing becomes visible to the eye.

When we lose our steady pound each week the loss is usually well distributed. The time comes nevertheless in every reducer's life when those around him discover his secret.

That is a joyful day. But it is also the heyday of the self-appointed consultants. Innocently, lovingly, filled with good intentions, friends and relatives go to work at wrecking your reducing program. In your slimmer neckline and trimmer face they see only signs of poor health. They take pity on you. They sympathize.

"Isn't your doctor too hard on you?" "Do you really think you should go on? I liked you better before." "I talked it over with my wife yesterday—we both wonder if anything is wrong."

A few such remarks are sufficient to make the most joyful reducer miserable and to haunt the best-balanced mind. "Are they right?" "Do I look bad?" "Maybe I am really sick?" And inevitably, "Shall I keep going? Perhaps I ought to take a vacation from reducing—"

These well-meaning wreckers are usually our nearest of kin, our dearest of friends, our closest working associates. They would be deeply hurt if they knew how much harm their unsought advice can do. They have brought to an end many slimming attempts within reach of success, and forced the victim back into overweight, to the detriment of his peace of mind and sometimes his health.

When this had happened to me several times my wife went into action. One day she came home with a sun-ray lamp.

"Get a sun tan," she said. "Summer or winter, the 'Miami look' will convince all your good friends that you are neither tired nor sick and they will stop shattering your peace with their worry. Nobody worries about people with a healthy tan."

The "Miami look" worked wonders. People stopped inquiring about my health. The tanned face convinced the world that I felt fine, and I was quietly allowed to lose another forty pounds without having to defend myself further against my friends.

Your perils may be different, and your weapons for self-defense may differ accordingly. Be sure that any worthwhile endeavor has its hazards, and be ready for them when they come. When you are really in doubt, there is always your doctor to check and reassure you. When you waver, when you would like to share your secret and be heartened on your reducing way, turn again to the Slim Gourmet and read a little here, a little there, about the many others who have followed this way to success.

And meanwhile, male or female, pay attention to looking well, and make the quick change to smaller sizes in clothes as the pounds and the inches melt away steadily, week by week.

17   WILL POWER HAS NOTHING

TO DO WITH REDUCING

"My kingdom for a pill!" a Shakespearean actress used to cry whenever the scales told her the unflattering truth. "Forty pounds is too much to be dieted away. Why don't you invent a pill so we can eat all we like and still lose? You could make millions with it."

She dreamed of her pill, starved the girth away, then gained it back. Starved and gained. She still lives in that unreal world of the permanent diet addict who dreams of slimming, falls for

every bold promise and experiments with any diet that advertises, "Lose 40 lbs. in 6 weeks!"

Years ago one of my business friends, a sober German
businessman, praised a sanitarium that capitalized on such
dreams. There they made the patient fast on an apple the first
two days, with similar tortures for four weeks under strict medical
supervision. He lost more than forty pounds in the process, and
his life shortly after. Dreams can be dangerous.

It takes quite a few years to assemble forty pounds of overweight. What is the good of making it disappear in a few weeks
—for a few months? Would it not be better to make it disappear
forever, even if it takes a little longer to do so? One pound a
week, the reducing maximum of the Slim Gourmet, is not an arbitrary figure. It is the result of personal experience, of observation of a great many other people, and also it is the only rate of
reducing to which no doctor will object for a healthy adult, according to the medical knowledge we have today. A pound a
week allows the reducer to reduce happily. That makes it the
only possible maximum to the Slim Gourmet.

A weekly calorie deficit of 3,500 calories (500 calories a day) is
all that is needed to lose one pound per week. It is not hard for a
154-pound man to reduce on an allowance of 14,000 calories a
week, nor for a woman of 150 pounds to reduce on an allowance
of 12,600 calories a week.

Reducing can be done joyfully, provided you don't ask too
much of yourself. Unfortunately many people still do.

Again and again I have heard the same self-accusation: "I
don't seem to have sufficient will power." Five people out of ten,
when hearing that I lost more than eighty pounds, say, "You
must have very strong will power."

It may sound paradoxical, but will power has nothing to do
with reducing. What people call "lack of will power" is often
only the refusal of our wiser self to obey demands that are
simply impossible to fulfill.

Is it lack of will power when four-year-old Teddy piles six

scoops of ice cream on his plate and cannot finish them? It is lack of judgment. It is his limited experience and knowledge that are responsible for his mistake.

As the German proverb goes, Teddy's "eyes were bigger than his stomach." The case of the people with "no will power" is usually not unlike Teddy's case. Their reducing hopes are larger than their eating personalities will stand for. I could read a peace-loving speech by Hitler and be unimpressed. I can read the advertisement of "Lose 20 lbs. in a week" without believing it. The reducing promise is like Hitler's promise of peace. Both are only armistices, one between two wars, the other between two overweight periods.

It was not a lack of will power that made you fail with your last diet. It was a lack of judgment on *the limitation of what is possible*.

Fed up with having to buy size 20 dresses or not fitting into ready-to-wear suits, we are all prone to let impatience and wishful thinking plan our reducing. Two pounds a week, five pounds a week, eight pounds a week—why not? The primitive in us all still believes in magic. "You can shed all your surplus weight in a month. It is worth while to suffer for it. After the 1,000-calorie diet comes size 10," the wishful self whispers.

Thousands of dieters fail for the few who succeed in this way. Are the thousands exceptional, or the few? After years of experience and study, of diet planning and diet results, I believe that those who fail to keep to the new weight after too rigid dieting are only reacting normally. It is a sign of mental and physical health to eat to excess after starvation.

Realistic reducing means only doing what is possible. The Slim Gourmet's way allows a maximum of one pound per week. But it need not be a pound a week for everybody. Some reduce better to the tune of three pounds a month or only two. To lose twenty-four to thirty pounds in a year—and lose it permanently —is surely nothing to be ashamed of!

The forty-five weekly habit-testers help you to find the exact range of what is possible for you. They may help you discover that you can change your overloaded breakfast to a lighter one. They may warn you not to eliminate the chocolate bar at eleven or four o'clock because your nervous system would rebel at that particular deprivation. The Slim Gourmet's food habit inventory, plus your habit tests, are designed to meet your own food personality. With their help you make your own reducing plan based on your food personality, your habits and your needs.

If you put thought, time, and realism into your planning, you need not worry about any weakness of your will power. You don't have to be a superman to succeed, nor is it proof of weakness if something goes wrong.

A realistic plan succeeds for the same reason the Empire State Building stands: the foundation and the structure are suited to the load. The engineer plans his load within the limits of the possible. Your reducing plans will succeed if you stay within the limits of what is possible for you.

After I had planned to lose seventy-eight pounds in eighteen months, I had to change my reducing strategy and my tactics from time to time. During one vacation month, mountain-climbing increased my energy-spending by 1,500 to 2,000 calories a day and I had to eat more than my reducing plan had called for. I might have lost more than my maximum pound a week by eating as though I were merely going to the office every day while instead I was engaging in a strenuous sport. I might have lost more, yes, but at the cost of enjoying my vacation—or of rebelliously giving up reducing altogether because it was impossibly hard. A really workable reducing plan works both ways. You lose the pound a week that you set out to lose, neither more nor less. Too much that is valuable is at stake for you to tamper with this maximum, including your happiness and comfort while reducing.

Some time later a sudden urge for sweets threatened to wreck the balance of my eating program. Should I have vowed not to eat sweets at all? I do not believe in these vows. The diet books say we get enough sugar from the fruits we eat. Who knows whether tomorrow's science will not discover that a little straight sugar now and then is a great boon for our health? In any case, my stomach shouted for sweets. I believe in listening to the stomach, even when it whispers. Could I ignore its shouting? So I built sweets into my eating program while reducing. I preferred changing my plan to turning a deaf ear to my sudden desire.

This realistic planning, this budget of slow reducing and the unswerving aim of one pound a week and no more under all circumstances makes slimming safe, successful, and enjoyable. If you are going to spend six, or twelve, or eighteen months reducing, those are months of living as well. Make them happy, and you will make your plan work.

18   THE SLIM GOURMET'S WAY

FOR THE HEAVY OVERWEIGHT

The champion eater of Germany and possibly of the world, who was photographed recently in *Life* magazine, consumes 9,400 calories a day. His "more than a dozen big steins of beer a day" themselves add up to about 3,600 calories and he eats sausages, cheese, pork chops, dumplings, potatoes, and rolls at six meals a day besides.

How much does this Bavarian carpenter actually overeat? Let's give him a big, a very big maintenance allowance, since he is after all a carpenter in the time he can spare between snacks. Even if he has a maintenance allowance of 5,900 calories a day, the highest I could put together, with this eating program he should be gaining a pound a day to add to the 277 pounds of his reported weight.

That is impossible. Either the *Life* reporter caught and photographed the man on an exceptional day, or he is one of those who pay every year for undisciplined eating with a month or more of strict fasting and a permanently bad eating conscience.

A hundred and thirty years ago no less a reporter than Brillat-Savarin observed a similar eccentric: in an alehouse on New York's Broadway, a man named Edward sat drinking ale from morning to night in plain view of all passersby. He measured five feet ten inches in height and had a waistline of eight feet.

Such freak-show diversions have become rare in the United States but are still encountered in countries where medieval eating habits survive. American travelers in Bavaria, Switzerland, and Denmark are often appalled by the sight of so many overweight men and women. In Holland the size most in demand in ladies' dress shops is not size 12 as in the United States but size 16.

The American state of overweight is quite different. Most overweight Americans overeat only a little each day, judging by my correspondents. My guess is that not more than five out of a hundred readers of this book will find at the end of their food habit inventory that they have been overeating to the extent of 1,000 or more calories daily.

Are those five heavy eaters also able to follow the Slim Gourmet's way? Can they also reduce in this gentle and pleasurable manner, without the hunger pangs of severe diets and the self-castigation of never eating what they most enjoy?

I do not know whether *Life*'s Bavarian carpenter or Brillat-Savarin's Broadway Edward, dedicated to suicide by eating, would be candidates for the Slim Gourmet's way. To all others, however, whether they overeat only 200 calories a day (thus gaining twenty pounds a year) or 500 calories (fifty pounds a year) the Slim Gourmet's system offers a safe and pleasant—and practical—way to reduce permanently. The heavy overeater will only have to climb down the calorie ladder more slowly than the others. It may take a few months until he reaches his calorie maintenance allowance, and a little longer to arrive at his reducing allowance. But the way is agreeable and easy, and anyone who wishes to divest himself of his fleshly burden can negotiate it with success.

Let us assume that your present eating is 3,500 calories a day and your maintenance allowance is 2,800. The steps downward need to be taken slowly and gradually to allow your eating personality to become accustomed to the new way of life. The schedule would be something like this:

During the first month, step down to 3,000 calories a day.

During the second month, cut to 2,800 calories a day. You are now at your maintenance allowance and no longer gaining weight.

By the third month, you are eating 2,500 calories daily, 300 calories less than your allowance, and you are beginning to lose weight. In this month you should lose two and one-half pounds.

With the fourth month you really begin to reduce the Slim Gourmet's way on a daily 2,300-calorie reducing allowance (16,100 calories a week), which relieves you of one pound a week with no damage to either your mental or physical health—or to your joy in eating.

I must warn the heavy overeater—one who eats more than 500 excess calories a day—not to take the plunge too suddenly. A gradual reduction of 500 calories a day during the first month is as much as you can reasonably ask of yourself. To do more is superhuman; to attempt more is to risk defeat and discouragement at the outset. With this reduction in your eating you have already achieved a great deal. Even if your scale shows that you are still gaining a pound or two during this month, you have taken a first step in the direction of permanent victory over your pounds, and proved to yourself that you are both intelligent and wise.

The next step puts a final end to your weight-gaining. Then, and then only, you begin to reduce in the security that this will be a reduction for all time, and that you will be able to live in health and peace of mind hereafter without fear of having to repeat this performance.

19   THE THREE-TO-FIVE-POUND WORRY

"Are you really interested only in people who must lose ten, twenty, fifty pounds? What about the rest of us who have only five or four or even three pounds to lose?" the lady from San Francisco demanded.

"But you surely have no weight problem!" I exclaimed.

"Nonsense. Everybody has a weight problem. There is not one woman I know," the lady from the Pacific shore went on, "who does not wish she could lose a few pounds once and for all. Every one of us worries when she eats a rich but delicious dish, or is tempted to take a second helping, or suddenly succumbs to a desire for an ice cream soda. We worry at cocktail parties and are frightened by the hors d'oeuvres before dinner. If we could once lose those five pounds, then we wouldn't worry about the occasional—the very occasional—indulgence."

Was it possible, I asked, that of the trim American women I have seen walking on Fifth Avenue and in Rittenhouse Square, on Michigan or Wilshire Boulevard, on Nob Hill in the lady's own beautiful city—was it possible that many among those slender American women worry about their weight?

It was not only possible, she assured me, but a fact. The three-to-five-pound worry clouded the joy of eating of many whose weight problem was their own well-kept secret.

Have these ladies a weight problem in reality? I remembered that some who have written to me from all over the country asking how they could lose weight were actually *underweight*.

So I turned to the reliable height-weight tables of the Metropolitan Life Insurance Company. For the benefit of the three-to-five-pound worriers I give the tables here:

DESIRABLE WEIGHTS FOR MEN OF AGES 25 AND OVER

Weight in Pounds According to Frame (as Ordinarily Dressed)

HEIGHT (WITH SHOES ON)		SMALL	MEDIUM	LARGE
FEET	INCHES	FRAME	FRAME	FRAME
5	2	116–125	124–133	131–142
5	3	119–128	127–136	133–144
5	4	122–132	130–140	137–149
5	5	126–136	134–144	141–153
5	6	129–139	137–147	145–157
5	7	133–143	141–151	149–162
5	8	136–147	145–156	153–166
5	9	140–151	149–160	157–170
5	10	144–155	153–164	161–175
5	11	148–159	147–168	165–180
6	0	152–164	161–173	169–185
6	1	157–169	166–178	174–190
6	2	163–175	171–184	179–196
6	3	168–180	176–189	184–202

DESIRABLE WEIGHTS FOR WOMEN OF AGES 25 AND OVER

Weight in Pounds According to Frame (as Ordinarily Dressed)

HEIGHT (WITH SHOES ON)		SMALL	MEDIUM	LARGE
FEET	INCHES	FRAME	FRAME	FRAME
4	11	104–111	110–118	117–127
5	0	105–113	112–120	119–129
5	1	107–115	114–122	121–131
5	2	110–118	117–125	124–135
5	3	113–121	120–128	127–138

HEIGHT (WITH SHOES ON)		SMALL	MEDIUM	LARGE
FEET	INCHES	FRAME	FRAME	FRAME
5	4	116–125	124–132	131–142
5	5	119–128	127–135	133–145
5	6	123–132	130–140	138–150
5	7	126–136	134–144	142–154
5	8	129–139	137–147	145–158
5	9	133–143	141–151	149–162
5	10	136–147	145–155	152–166
5	11	139–150	148–158	155–169

These figures are neither statutes nor laws. They are based on the weights of hundreds of thousands of men and women of age twenty-five and over, and according to the present state of medical knowledge they are considered the healthiest weights for adults of each sex, the "desirable" weights, as the life insurance company delicately puts it.

We also know that a little more or a little less—say five pounds per hundred above or below these "desirable" averages—is still normal. No man need worry if he tips the scale at 170 when the table suggests 166, nor a woman if she weighs 129 instead of 124. These small differences have no influence whatever on health or life expectancy. We near the danger zone only when the scale goes more than ten pounds per hundred above our desirable weight. If we weigh 150 or more when we should weigh 136, then it is time to think about a sensible program of reducing.

Yet I see the point of the lady from San Francisco. It is surely better to be "desirable" than merely normal. There is no reason why one should not shrink off three or four or five pounds and with them the weight-worry that casts a shadow on the pleasure of eating. Once you shed them, and know how easy it is to keep them shed, there is no longer any room for anxiety at the dinner table.

It is a pity for anyone to be troubled by these few extra

pounds and the fear of continuing to gain when it is so small a task to deal with them. No magic is involved, only common sense. It may be that merely reading this book twice will do the trick. Many people who have talked over the Slim Gourmet's way with me have reported afterward that they began to lose weight with no effort that they or those around them could see. They "could not help" thinking about their food habits, and applying to their daily eating a few of the Slim Gourmet's principles that most appealed to them. After a few weeks the scale notified them that their few troublesome pounds had melted away like snow in the sun.

Following the Slim Gourmet's way is the same whether the weight to be lost is five pounds or fifty-five. The difference is only in time, not in method. The Food Habit Inventory, the search for the Reasons Why, and the Weekly Habit-Testing are the tools for effortlessly arriving at that "desirable" weight and figure—and staying there. Five pounds take five weeks. It is as simple as that.

There is a little danger all its own in the three-to-five-pound worry. Just when the problem concerns "only a few pounds," just then do we fall victims to the illusion that the job can be done in one sitting, with a 1,000-calorie cure.

Fasting one day will do it, we tell ourselves. Or two weeks at 1,000 calories—and the five pounds are gone.

That is indisputable—in theory. But life is not logical, and it persists in proving this logical theory incorrect. Weight too quickly lost is not lost but only absent. It lurks in the eating habits we have not really explored or understood, and sneaks back as soon as we return to normal living. Furthermore, the harsh punishment of a starvation diet, even when briefly followed, leaves its scars. Fear and guilt become our table companions.

The three-to-five-pound worry is unrealistic according to the height-weight charts, but the habits that put on those extra pounds can also put on more. Five pounds too many may be the beginning of a road to overweight that ends with twenty.

So it is well to take a good look into the secrets of your food personality, and abolish the three-to-five-pound worry once and for all.

Book Three

THE JOY OF EATING

From Tennessee Mrs. H. wrote a desperate letter. She has been dieting for two years, quite successfully, but "the moment I eat one bite of bread, the pounds begin to pile on again."

Mrs. H.'s diet calls for "no bread." "There is a health bread here that has no fat added, and many are using it," she writes. "But my diet says no bread at all. I love bread or crackers most of all but haven't had but very little in twenty months. I'd rather have one piece of buttered toast or one small biscuit for breakfast than any meal."

With this letter Mrs. H. sent the label of the health bread, which states that a slice counts for only 44 calories. But her ready-made diet says, "no bread" and Mrs. H. follows the diet —except when her pent-up longing for bread is too strong, and then every slice she eats adds calories to her diet. It also adds weight. And it adds guilt.

Mrs. H. lost twenty pounds, but she feels something is wrong with her success. I feel it too, because two weeks after the Slim Gourmet's articles had begun to appear in her local paper, I had already received twenty pages in letters from her, closely handwritten, giving me the sad story of her successful dieting. She has lost weight but also her joy in life. She has dieted successfully but missed the pleasure of eating. She has denied herself the bread she loves and can no longer stand the boiled beef she loathes.

Mrs. H. is one of thousands who have said or written to me the same words: "I love bread," and the same complaint that "a meal without bread is no meal."

> *"The cry of nature we must heed—*
> *Bread we want and bread we need."*

Thus writes a Frenchman, Pierre Dupont. Perhaps he remembered a naïve French queen, Marie Antoinette, who also could not understand when her ministers told her, "The people want bread." (But we must recall, to her credit, that she answered, "Let them eat cake!" She did not say, like the diet dictator, "They can do without bread.")

The need for bread is universal and cannot be pooh-poohed by diet designers. The command, "no bread," is too lightly written into many a slimming diet. The special meaning that bread has for human beings is worthy of serious consideration. I would even go further and say that to ignore it is to endanger at least the success of a reducing program, and perhaps to endanger health itself.

It is easy enough to compose a diet without the two rolls or the three or four slices of bread or toast that most of us eat every day. Any accountant can do it, and celebrate his achievement by multiplying the 200 calories he has "saved" each day by 365: 73,000 calories a year! There must be many such accountant-nutritionists to whom a diet is successful if its calorie accounting looks good on paper. They can never have tried earnestly to live with such a diet; otherwise their own experience would have told them that they cannot abolish six thousand years of history with a stroke of the typewriter.

Since long before Moses led the Children of Israel out of Egypt, carrying their unleavened loaves, bread has been the centerpiece of man's eating as a human being rather than as an animal. Historians and scholars, anthropologists and archaeologists can tell the nutritionists what bread means to man. Any minister, priest, or rabbi can give the answer. Man lives not by bread alone, but most religions teach us to honor divine Providence in the symbol of bread, and give thanks before every meal by a benediction of bread.

Bread plays an indispensable part not only in the religious practice of peoples of the Western world but also in the life of man as a civilized, social being. "Breaking bread" means communicating with our fellow men. "Sharing one's bread" is an expression of human charity. "Earning one's bread and butter" means making a living.

Bread is far more than merely another foodstuff. It is the supreme symbol of food and hence of life itself. This is so in our civilization and in the many cultures that preceded ours. It is a daring diet dictator indeed who dismisses it with the two little words, "no bread!"

There are two other potent reasons why bread cannot be excluded from our meals. It is a relatively inexpensive food. And it is one of the most delicious foods we can enjoy.

The Slim Gourmet would never try to reduce by abandoning bread, or suggest that anyone else should do so. His philosophy would not exclude bread from even the strictest diet. He would ask instead, "Which breads do you like?" "Do you know enough about bread and its varieties to get the best in taste and enjoyment out of it?"

When asked, "How do you feel about bread?" some few people will shrug their comparative indifference to it. But most—

like myself, like Mrs. H., and thousands of my correspondents—
will answer unhesitatingly, "I love it." For all of us bread-lovers
it is obvious that bread cannot safely be left out of our reducing
program. But the Slim Gourmet believes that also for those who
are not conscious of any dependence upon bread, it is wiser to
give this good and significant product of man's ingenuity a
place, however small, at the table even while slimming. If we
could do without bread would we call it the staff of life?

For us who know the high place bread holds in our food af-
fections, a true appreciation of its quality can actually help our
slimming. The Slim Gourmet believes that we should never eat
any food without putting our minds to what we are eating. Because it is so necessary to us and so familiar, we tend to take our
bread for granted. The diet designers who forbid us our bread
have this on their side at least: we eat our bread inattentively
and thus we eat too much of it. We are actually not aware of
bread until the reducing dictators take it away from us! But
bread is precisely one of the items on the menu that deserves
attention and discrimination.

In England I do not eat much bread because only rarely can
I get good bread there. The British are not expert at bringing
out the best in many foods, and they do not generally know the
art of baking bread that tastes.

Across the Channel, however, lies France, where men of all
persuasions and parties are united in appreciation of one of the
best breads to be found in the world. And on this side of the
Atlantic, our own United States can be called the paradise of
bread-eaters.

American bread varieties are legion. Consider the choice pre-
sented in our supermarkets alone, not to mention the many
French, Italian, and Jewish bakeshops which offer additional
oven-baked breads or handmade old-fashioned breads and rolls.
We can eat white or whole wheat or cracked wheat bread, protein bread, milk bread, potato bread, rasin and cinnamon bread
either plain or mixed, rye bread either sweet or sour or salty

and in many shades of light and dark; all these are packaged and mass-distributed. We can buy Boston brown bread and johnny cake, Irish soda bread and pumpernickel, spoon bread and graham bread, Portuguese bread and Swedish *limpa* bread, matzoth and Italian *grissini*, plain and sweet rolls and scones and buns in dozens of shapes and flavors.

The Slim Gourmet, who chooses what he eats and knows the food he is eating, has a rich choice. For my part, I eat not one but all the breads I like. Each morning I have two different kinds of bread at the breakfast table. The second is there to remind me to select one or the other, or to taste a little of each— in other words, to enjoy consciously instead of absent-mindedly gobbling up my bread.

A distinguished churchman, who is obliged to dine out a great deal, always asks his host or the waiter to substitute his favorite rye bread for the customary dinner roll. One of our prominent film stars goes so far as to carry her own special bread in her handbag. "Most rolls don't agree with me," she explains tactfully, but in fact she is exercising her right to enjoy consciously the bread she likes, wherever she may be.

My friend L. has become a successful reducer, but only since together we invented the Slim Gourmet's Bread-Tasting Day. My friend does not merely like bread. He loves it like a lover, missing it when it is not around, suffering when it is banned from his menus. He eats it wherever he finds it, in whatever form and with whatever trimming.

Sweet butter, salt butter, jam, honey, cottage cheese, cream cheese, and any combination that may fit are a welcome part of his enjoyment of bread. To him, as to many, a slice or two of bread is medicine to overcome mental strain and a ritual to give authority to a meal, as well as a natural and wholesome way to satisfy hunger.

But, left to himself, he was also eating bread in *quantity*. Bread, eaten to excess, can add inches to one's girth. Something had to be done.

"What would you say to a bread day, one day a week?" I asked him. "For breakfast, lunch, dinner, snacks, nothing but bread?" He was curious and interested.

So we composed a Bread-tasting Day, not forgetting that it would be good only if it conformed to the rules of the Slim Gourmet. In other words, our composition of tastes had to be so good that less quantity would satisfy us.

Thus we came to the first menu, which is set down here not as a pattern for everybody but as an example of how this can be done:

		CALORIES
Breakfast:	1 cup of black coffee	—
	1 roll with thin layer of cream cheese	100
	1 buttered toast with jam	150
Luncheon:	1 cup of consommé	50
	1 rye sandwich with Swiss cheese and ham	350
	2 pcs. French bread without trimming, just to taste it when it is fresh	100
	1 cup of black coffee	—
Coming-home Snack:	10 *grissini*	150
	1 apple	100
Dinner:	a gourmet's plate to choose from:	
	6 breads in small slices: sour rye French bread Boston brown pumpernickel enriched wheat whole grain wheat	300
	with cheese, radishes, a hard-boiled egg, butter, ham, salami	300
	1 glass of good wine	75

Late Snack:	10 *grissini*	150
	1 glass tomato juice	50
TOTAL		1,875

My friend L.'s slow-reducing allowance for this year is 2,000 calories a day. Thus on our Bread-tasting Day we still have a reserve of 125 calories to keep, if we like, for possible mistakes in counting.

This Slim Gourmet's Bread-tasting Day was the first. L. has since refined the original program considerably. With his collector's nose he has been discovering new breads in known and unknown bakeries to adorn each week's bread feast, and he enjoys his bread tasting in the same way Frank Schoonmaker enjoys wine tasting.

The Bread-tasting Day achieved two great results for him. It made his beloved bread a key to the Slim Gourmet's world of better eating. And it made him less bread-hungry during the week. One day set aside to satisfy the bread preference of his food character took out of his unconscious eating habits the automatic bread-gulping and the unavoidable weight gains that come when you don't take your mind with you to the table.

There may be people who can live without bread, and who can be advised to reduce by banning bread from the menu. For them, I have discovered, bread is not a source of much weight and going entirely breadless contributes little to their reducing program. But perhaps my bread philosophy will help the many bread lovers to rebel successfully against the dietitians.

21   WHY NOT POTATOES?

It had to be precisely a lady from Quito, who at my dinner table refused a most exquisite table delight: medium-sized, mealy Idaho potato, baked and spiced with a mixture of spring onions and herbs melting in a pat of butter.

"But don't you know potatoes are fattening?" she said. That's what they learn nowadays in Quito, where the sixteenth-century Spaniards met the potato for the first time.

The others knew better and ate the divine dish with great gusto. The Ecuadorian lady, a little abashed by my silence, played with her knife and a roll and the butter.

"Or have you also a new theory on the potato? Don't tell me you are reducing at this meal!"

"Pardon," I said, "I did not answer you at once because I wanted to eat this alluring dish while it was hot.

"Of course you will not overeat at the Slim Gourmet's table," I continued, "and the baked Idaho you have not eaten is no more fattening than the buttered roll you just ate. Forget the calories for a moment. They measure only energy. Have you ever measured the cheer that a well-baked, earthy potato gives you, the satisfying aftertaste it leaves, the toothsome enchantment it produces when served with this buttered spice and onion flavoring?"

Potatoes are no more fattening than oranges, if you eat them sensibly and don't make a routine of potato eating like the Dutch potato eaters, whose greed and poverty van Gogh has depicted so well in his famous painting.

The Idaho or the California potato or the Blue Christy potato from Maine are not only good and mealy, delectable and just the right size for Slim Gourmets, they are also one of the healthiest meals we can buy in our market. In them you eat calcium and brain-nourishing phosphorus. They give you Vitamin A and thiamine, riboflavin and niacin, ascorbic acid and a whole spectrum of other important nutrients.

Of course you can gain weight on potatoes, if you eat them the Belgian way. In that country they kill the personality of the potato by eating all of the year's varieties, throughout the year, deep-fried. They grow rather stout on this regime but it is not the potato that does it, it is the fat. Fat not only kills the taste of the potato but also increases its food value to unnecessary heights, as the waistlines of the Belgian potato eaters clearly show.

The Slim Gourmet never eats without tasting. I knew a man from Holland who could name the potatoes that were served, simply by their taste, provided they were baked or boiled the right way. He would tell you whether you served him a Green Mountain from Vermont or an Irish Cobbler from Massachusetts, a Dakota Red or a Massaba. He was a potato connoisseur —and he was trim and lean as a pine tree.

The Slim Gourmet is quite satisfied to eat one potato. He leaves mass consumption to careless diners who never know what they are eating. He therefore never can gain weight on potatoes.

"You remind me," the lady from Quito said, "it is really only the little new potato we eat as a treat, with parsley and butter. The others are considered routine."

Of course the new potatoes have a special flavor. There are many in our markets in spring. The best I ever ate were those from Malta and Cyprus; they are rather yellowish and are the only potatoes that must be firm instead of mealy. Frying them would really be barbarian. The best way to eat them is boiled in their skins and with tiny bits of butter.

It seems it is a law of Nature that new potatoes cannot be eaten the whole year round. There are even times when only one variety of potato is available and it is up to the Slim Gourmet to bring variety into his potato eating. In any case the potato will not appear too often on his table. He avoids routine above all and anything that is eaten daily would be routine and therefore dangerous. I love the baked potato, but, eaten too often, even the baked potato would become routine and we therefore have to invent other preparations.

Boiled potatoes are wonderful, provided they are dry. The Dutch are great masters in the art of boiling potatoes and bringing them to the table as a mouth-watering dish. They boil potatoes in the usual way, but they remove the pot from the fire when a speared potato falls off the fork. After the water has been poured off, the pot is put back on a low flame until the potatoes are dry as paper. The pot must be shaken once or twice to keep the potatoes from burning.

Baking and boiling are the ways to eat potatoes and enjoy their taste. Taste, however, is too personal a matter for everyone to agree with this dictum. It is quite possible that you like mashed potatoes or potato salad or potato soup, or that potato chips may be necessary for your nerves.

If you don't make a routine out of potato eating or any other one-dish favoritism, eat potatoes at your pleasure. The potato in itself is not fattening. When you eat potato salad with mayonnaise, I would advise you to consult your calorie chart. A cupful of this dish may cost you 400-500 calories. There may be days when 400 calories are no longer available, and on such days potato salad would not be a good choice.

For those who want to make taste excursions with potatoes I report: The French have sixty kinds of food they combine with potatoes. They like to eat potatoes with onions, herbs, bacon, butter, truffles, sausage meat, garlic, or tomatoes; with three or four kinds of cheese; with cream, eggs, or spinach, and simply with pepper and salt.

To all these I prefer potatoes baked in their jackets. Once a month they are a must on the Slim Gourmet's table.

22   CHEESE FANCIERS

ARE USUALLY SLIM

"No cheese except cottage cheese" was the dictum of one of the hunger diets that made me lose weight only to gain it back soon afterward.

The deprived soul who designed this diet had probably never known the taste of the pale golden paste that flows out of a ripe French Brie when a knife is pressed upon it. His was a diet for food automatons and not for living human beings. Was he, like the ancient Chinese, prejudiced against the curd of the milk? Or was he merely one of those diligent technicians who make diet programs by looking for the low-calorie foods on the calorie charts where taste, quality, and joy are buried in the cold print of statistics?

Had the poor man never experienced the glory of an old, marbled cheddar cheese eaten with an apple, with a sip of coffee, or its sharp taste blended with the mellowness of bourbon?

Could he perhaps be a pernicious foe of the United States, seeking to wreck the American economy by discouraging the sale of the approximately four hundred million pounds of cheddar the government holds in stock? An enemy of the state of Wisconsin, glorious for its native cheeses and its fine adaptations of foreign cheeses? A foe of the French, who do a brisk export trade in the products of their cheese-making artists? Of the Dutch, who are masters at aging cheese?

I think this fad-diet dictator can properly be declared an enemy of the human race, sinning against one of mankind's best and oldest friends. A good cheese is so satisfying to the palate, so filling to the appetite, that a cube costing no more than 100 calories can substitute for the richest, highest-calorie dessert. This is why cheese fanciers are usually slim. And we have not even mentioned its high value in proteins and other nutrients that rank cheese with meat, fish, and eggs among the basic foods. Even the Chinese, opposed as they traditionally are to milk curds, make a kind of cheese out of soya beans. Thus the whole world can unite against the diet designer's wholesale condemnation of cheese for the weight-conscious.

Brillat-Savarin, the nineteenth-century law-giver for gourmets, wrote, "A dessert without cheese is like a beauty who lacks an eye." Another spirited Frenchman said, "Cheese is the crown of a good meal and the supplement of a poor one." The Slim Gourmet adds, "Show me how you eat cheese and I will tell you who you are."

The success of the French cheese purveyor, M. Androuet, with his cheese display at the New York World's Fair, the many well-stocked cheese specialty shops all over the United States, the resplendent cheese counters in the delicacy shops of the great department stores and especially the forty or fifty different kinds of American and imported cheese in all the larger super-markets—these are sure signs of the refinement of eating culture in this country. It is no longer true, as a recent but in this respect obsolete gastronomical encyclopedia observes, that "Americans are not great cheese eaters." Americans have graduated from the time when they were tricked into eating cheese by finding a piece of it on the plate with every slice of apple pie.

There must be millions of discriminating cheese fanciers in the United States. For them, and for the new adepts of the Slim Gourmet's art of eating, I will now disclose how one can eat and appreciate cheese, and at the same time reduce the Slim Gourmet's way.

Why was our anti-cheese diet designer so afraid of cheese for reducers? Because his calorie chart showed that four ounces of a hard cheese like American cheddar or Wisconsin Swiss count for 400 calories, while four ounces of fresh strawberries, for example, count only for 41 calories. That is very true on paper. It makes as much sense to point out that ten ounces of beer add up to only 115 calories while ten ounces of Scotch make 570 calories. The little mistake in accounting is merely that we are used to drinking ten ounces of beer but we take only one or two ounces of Scotch. It is also true that we may eat four ounces of strawberries but never the same quantity of cheddar cheese.

It may be that of skimmed-milk cottage cheese we are easily able to eat a four-ounce portion, happy in the knowledge that we have added only 101 calories to our calorie intake. Only a glutton, however, would eat such a portion of cheddar or Swiss. Of these cheeses, the average portion is about one ounce, and the caloric value of this ounce is equal to the four ounces of unadorned skimmed-milk cottage cheese. The difference is that the taste of cheddar is much more interesting, and the freedom to choose whatever cheese we want to eat brings a joy of eating that is unknown to the followers of hunger diets.

Some time ago at a restaurant I asked the waiter to serve me Philadelphia cream cheese instead of butter with the rolls at dinner. My guests were politely surprised until they discovered that Philadelphia cream cheese as a spread in place of butter introduced a new taste pleasure to their food vocabulary—and saved about 30 calories with each roll. We are frightened away from this cheese, one of the great cheeses of America, by the fact that an ounce of it counts for more than 100 calories. But we don't need an ounce of it. We can enjoy its velvety smoothness fully with half an ounce. Should not reducers have this right?

It may be difficult, for those who are just beginning to develop their taste, to distinguish between the flavors of wild rice and polished rice. They will have no such trouble tasting the differences between a Swiss cheese and a cheddar, a Camembert and a Brie. Cheese *is* taste. The many kinds of cheeses we can obtain in the smallest town are easily distinguishable and enjoyable.

Once the mind has been opened to these taste differences, we no longer need big portions to bring the taste message home. A one-inch cube tells the whole tale, and a second one helps us not to forget too soon the uniqueness of the treat.

To use cheese well during the reducing period, I recommend first of all enlarging your cheese vocabulary. Sample all the kinds you can find, and choose those you like well enough to want to eat again.

The second step is to find out your personal portion size of the different kinds of cheeses you have chosen as your favorites. For this you will balance the pleasure you take in the particular cheese and the number of calories you want to allot to it in place of some other food of equal calorie value.

The third step will be to replace many usual desserts, especially the thoughtlessly eaten sweet and sirupy puddings, the pies and pastries, with one of your chosen cheeses. Do not think of cheese any longer as merely a companion of pie. Eat your cheese by itself with or without coffee, with or without a cracker or a thin slice of pumpernickel or other bread.

Where do we begin with the enlargement of our cheese vocabulary? A survey of your refrigerator is a good place to start. How many different kinds of cheese are stored there at this moment? If there are only one or two, your cheese vocabulary is in real need of enlargement. If there are five or six, you have the makings of a cheese fancier and it will be easy for you to use your love of cheese for your reducing program. Whatever you find in the refrigerator, however, whether few or many cheeses, this is only the beginning of your cheese vocabulary inventory.

Now sit down for a moment and write down on a piece of paper the names of all other cheeses that come to your mind. If those that have already been mentioned in this chapter are unknown to you, leave them out. If you have eaten them, add them to your list, as you take stock of the present state of your cheese knowledge.

It would be interesting now to do some experimenting. If you put down American cheese, which is cheddar cheese, for instance, and if you like this cheese, on your next visit to a supermarket or to one of the little cheese shops that spring up like mushrooms nowadays, buy cheddar cheese in different stages of ripeness. The cheese shops usually have fresh, old, and very old cheddar. Instead of buying half a pound of one kind, buy three ounces of each.

If you noted that you like Swiss cheese, buy some Wisconsin Swiss and at the same time for comparison a small quantity of imported Swiss. Should you be able to find the two kinds which we import from Switzerland, Gruyère and Emmenthal, sample both, and make yourself an expert in Swiss cheese while you are learning what you really like most.

The same system can be followed with Edam cheese, which is made in a wonderful quality domestically but is quite another cheese in the original that comes from Holland, although from the outside it looks like our homemade version.

Should cottage cheese be one of your choices, you will learn from a quick survey at your food store that this cheese also has many varieties: California style, skimmed-milk, or creamed cottage cheese; cottage cheese with chives, with pimento; pot cheese, the Italian ricotta, and others besides.

The processed cheeses of different manufacturers have different tastes though they may bear similar names, because each brand has its own recipe. It may be revealing to buy the same cheese under two or three different labels and taste them, to make up your mind which you like most (but don't be influenced by the fact that one manufacturer's advertising is more alluring than another's).

This is only the beginning of your higher education in the fine art of cheese-tasting. Great treats are in store for you. The traditional European cheeses, whether they are imported or made in the United States, are ready to reveal their taste secrets to you. Don't be afraid of foreign-sounding names. You are not expected to pronounce them as the natives do. Don't be afraid of disappointments. My present cheese vocabulary comprises about forty cheeses, but it is the result of taste experiments with more than two hundred. There must have been many disappointments, but I have long forgotten them, and it was worthwhile to discover that I liked as many as forty cheeses and can vary my enjoyment of cheese that much.

To keep disappointment from marring your enjoyment of cheese at the very start, however, I recommend beginning with the king of cheeses, the cheese most people like best, the cheese that has been recommended by the greatest gourmets, the cheese that has been praised in song and poetry, the cheese that does not lose any of its great quality even when transported from faraway France to the West Coast of the United States. I recommend that you discover the mildness and sweetness, the creamy, soft, velvety, and thoroughly satisfying taste of the great original French Brie.

Brie is a very ancient cheese. It was known, praised, and sung as early as the sixteenth century. It is a farm-made, whole milk, creamy cheese. It is at its best between November and March, when the autumn Brie is on the market. Cheese made in spring and summer is inferior because the milk of French cows is poor after the long winter months. Many makers of Brie send their product to the United States. I prefer those that come from the neighborhood of Paris. Good Brie should be soft and its paste should have a rich yellow color. The crust is reddish and should be firm but not too pebbly. There is no objection to keeping Brie under refrigeration, provided you take it out and give it breathing time before it is brought to the table. An hour out of the refrigerator will do.

Nobody has to eat much of this poetic cheese (which, by the way, is eaten *with* the crust) to become aware of its mild and yet unique taste. My personal portion size is no larger than a box of Swedish matches (about half the size of a box of American matches). This, on half a slice of pumpernickel, or divided on two cheese crackers, rates among the best desserts I can think of, especially when the accompanying drink is a dry red wine.

Now we contrast the mildness of Brie with the sharp bite of Canadian cheddar, a wonderful luncheon finale and a great thrill for the palate if eaten with stalks of raw celery. Or try a spicy *nokkelost* from Norway, made from skimmed milk with cloves and caraway seed.

If you prefer a sweet mild cheese there is also a mild cheddar sold all over the country, which is younger than the aged, cured Canadian variety, and therefore much less expensive. For mildness there is also the Muenster from Wisconsin, or the Italian provolone, or the soft and rich product of Italian pastures, the Bel Paese, which is so well reproduced in Wisconsin that the most refined tongue cannot taste the difference.

I cannot say much about German and Czech cheeses like Limburger or Olmutzer, which have reappeared in some American delicatessen shops, as I myself do not like their taste and aftertaste. Neither can I grow enthusiastic about the taste of the original American Liederkranz. I have somehow never succeeded in eating this cheese at the right time. Either I got it overripe or not yet fully developed, and what I tasted could never compare with Getmesost from Sweden or the Wisconsin Muenster.

The cheese that is satisfying at all ages, whether it is young and still white, or old, crumbling, and green as marble is the Roquefort cheese that comes from France and is made from ewe's milk. The longer this cheese is cured in the damp caves of the town of Roquefort, the more it ferments and the better it tastes. I will never forget my visit to those caves, where I was privileged to taste a cheese that had been curing there for more than a year. It was so rich in the blue veins characteristic of this cheese that hardly any white was to be seen. The taste was too special to be described in mere words.

A similar cheese made from milk and cream, the English Stilton, comes immediately next in my scale of cheeses. When a

Stilton is ripe, the English make a hole in the loaf and pour sherry into it. Then they eat it with a spoon. One does not, of course, have to live in England to enjoy this sherry Stilton treat. I have enjoyed it with American Stilton and with Italian Gorgonzola, another cheese of the same type.

Slim Gourmets are of course satisfied with one or two teaspoons of this great and somewhat robust dessert.

Gorgonzola has recently appeared on the market in the rare form of "white Gorgonzola." This has a distinctive bitter flavor that is equaled by no other cheese in the world.

In the eyes of many who cherish our civilization, the invention of a new cheese is looked upon as a greater blessing to humanity than the invention of a new atom-smashing process. The little village of Camembert in Normandy, France, raised a statue to a Madame Harel because at the time of the French Revolution this remarkable woman invented a cheese which has made the name of this hamlet a household word to people who know good foods everywhere in the world.

Thicker in shape than Brie and usually sold in wedges that happen to have exactly 100 calories, the Camembert imported from Normandy has an orange colored crust and a smooth white-to-yellow paste which should be soft and yet not runny. It is very rarely that the original Camembert arrives on our shores in the right state of ripeness and taste. The cheese made for export to this country must be made with pasteurized milk because of our Food and Drug Act, and this is another reason why it is hard to find a satisfactory Norman Camembert on American tables.

We can, however, do very well without it, since we have American Camembert. Whether I am alone or have guests, about an hour before going to bed I remember to take one of the little Camembert wedges out of the refrigerator and let it warm up and breathe. American Camembert seems to me the greatest bedtime snack ever discovered. It is the right overture to sweet dreams.

This chapter on cheeses could go on and on. There are two hundred varieties of cheeses to be discovered, tasted, and registered by your palate and your memory. Cheese is the piano of the Slim Gourmet. Cheese brings harmony to any meal, and harmonious eating frees you from the gluttony of the thoughtless.

23   TEMPTATION AND APPLES

Did Eve really eat an apple? Was this the fruit from which she learned good and evil? The Bible does not reveal which fruit it was; it tells us only that she used fig leaves as the first material for clothes. Biblical scholars believe it was a fig the serpent recommended. Why did popular legend give Eve an apple?

Unfortunately we can find nowhere in Dr. Freud's or his successors' writings an explanation of this quite universal misreading of the sacred text. Without Freud's help I am left to the interpretation that is obvious to an ardent admirer of apples. Bible readers naturally assumed that Eve succumbed so readily to the serpent's suggestion because she was already tempted by the attractive fruit on the Tree of Knowledge. So they asked themselves, "What fruit could it be that so tempted her?" and chose the most alluring fruit known to them—the apple.

They knew from experience that apples not only advertise their deliciousness but also keep their promise. They may have had other reasons that I cannot guess, but whatever their reasons, early in the third century, they accorded to the apple the honor of tempting Eve, and in the twentieth century the legend is as vigorous as ever. Ask any company, wherever the Bible is read and known, what was the fruit that Eve ate. Nine out of ten will answer, "Eve ate an apple, of course!" and will be surprised to hear that it is not at all certain she did.

We can conclude from this little excursion into Biblical scholarship that apples have been considered the most tempting of the fruits through many, many centuries. I myself feel in tune with the taste of civilized society from antiquity to the present when I confess to a predilection for this kingly fruit and advise readers, gourmets, and especially reducers, to join me in its enjoyment.

The glory of the apple has been somewhat tarnished in recent years. Utilitarian and medical propaganda have dimmed the apple's popularity with wise and thrifty people who would relish it still as a great culinary treat which is also inexpensive.

"An apple a day keeps the doctor away" may be true. But the slogan puts the apple on the same platform with vitamin pills and bacteria-killing toothpastes. It deprives this divine fruit of its rightful place in the company of oysters, asparagus, lobsters, sirloin steaks, peaches, and all the other noble foods that make our eating gracious.

Forget the doctor and forget about eating "apples." Eat a Winesap or a red Delicious, and muster all your tasting capacities to enjoy the juicy and crisp, sweet and slightly tart, and above all the satisfying, fruit which actually comes from a domesticated rosebush and is botanically called an apple.

The Greeks named Aphrodite, the goddess of Beauty and Love, the protectress of apples. It may have been the influence of Greek culture on Jews and early Christians that merged Aphrodite and the apple with Mother Eve. Legends were antiquity's advertising. Adding Eve's testimonial for the apple to Aphrodite's—and also Helen of Troy's—was one way of distinguishing a choice fruit from the many.

But let us accept the legend. Eve may really have been tempted by the serpent and the apple. And let us give the apple, the hundred varieties that grow in the United States, its new role—as a mighty weapon *against* temptation.

"If I am hungry, nervous, or depressed, I raid the icebox," a correspondent writes. Who does not know this experience when eating becomes irrational, when we stand in the kitchen and without counting or really enjoying what we eat we add hundreds of calories to our daily allowance!

"When I get home from work I have to eat something—it helps me forget the worries of the day—"

"I have to eat between meals—otherwise I overeat at dinner or thoughtlessly eat rolls and butter—"

"A sandwich before the cocktail party is a must for hungry diplomats—" I heard this last in Washington where cocktail parties are part of everyone's job, or so it appears.

Human nature is by no means rational. Even the strongest will to reduce is subject to many temptations and demands that we cannot deal with reasonably because they are not reasonable to begin with. We cannot always, under all circumstances, behave like Slim Gourmets.

A hundred such indulgences, a hundred such instances of irrational eating, a hundred 300-calorie snacks which have not been budgeted beforehand may add nine pounds to our weight in a year. They frustrate our reducing and give us a bad conscience.

I have been protected against such episodes by apples. There is always the prospect of one of several different apple varieties waiting for me whether I am at home or in the office, in the kitchen or in the dining room. The sight alone of these beautiful, perfectly designed fruits soothes my conscious and subconscious appetites. When an unscheduled desire for something to eat threatens to overwhelm me, I can always eat an apple.

There are only a few months in the year when I have to do without apples. From July to September, strawberries, cherries, peaches, plums, grapes and pears take their place. Even if apples are available during those months they are not at the peak of their taste. Apple growers have assured me that modern methods of transportation and storage theoretically preserve the original taste of apples even during the summer, but in my experience this theoretical promise is so rarely kept that I have made it a practice not to spoil my apple enjoyment by eating one that happens to be inferior because something went wrong with the storage.

My summer apple vacation makes me all the more eager for the reappearance of apples in October. It is a feast when I can buy, at the beginning of the month, the first new McIntosh apples in the best United States fancy quality. I add to my enjoyment of them with a few of the fresh walnuts that nature provides at the same season.

There are seventy-five hundred varieties of apples grown in the world. Not all are grown for commercial use. Many never leave the orchard where they grew and thousands are of a quality suitable only for cooking.

The best apples are grown in the United States. The world fame of the apples grown in the State of Washington is too well known for me to sing their praises here. The tastes of our apples are most varied. The inexperienced eater usually begins by liking the sweet apples, and graduates through the moderately tart ones to the hard, crisp, very tart varieties which are the choice of the apple gourmet.

Red Delicious and golden Delicious please the taste of almost everyone. From these the apple-taster goes on to McIntosh, Jonathan, and York Imperial. When he can distinguish among these, he comes to the greatest taste thrill in store for the American apple eater: the Winesap and Ben Davis. The Ben Davis is a particular favorite of a French gourmet friend of mine, who considers the French yellow and red Calvilles superior to our red and golden Delicious, but welcomes the unique Ben Davis as soon as it arrives each year in France.

My apple year begins with the McIntosh in October. November and December are the months for the red and golden Delicious. These apples can be bought in giant sizes, beautiful to look at, but for taste I prefer them in their middle sizes; the largest taste to me quite different. If you like to be precise you can measure them: my apple is three inches in diameter.

In January and February I eat mainly Jonathans and York Imperials. Then comes March, the great month when the Winesap is at its peak of juicy fragrance and displays all its powers of temptation to which not only Eve and Adam but everybody who enjoys good eating must succumb.

In the spring the Winesap, Baldwin, and Ben Davis are plentiful in all our markets. March and April are the months when two or three varieties of apples are always to be found in the Slim Gourmet's house. Then the apple year ends on a muted note in June, when the yellow Newtown makes its bow and the Slim Gourmet turns to the family of strawberries.

Though in the Bible the apple was the symbol of temptation, while I was reducing I found many ways of using apples to fight temptation. I used to eat an apple before I went out to a dinner party or before guests arrived at home. This was my way of never going hungry to the table and keeping my personal portion size always under control.

A word of warning is in order here for all believers in "fattening" and "reducing" foods. Since all foods contain calories, it is simple arithmetic that there are neither fattening nor reducing foods, and I would not like you to think that I am speaking of apples as a reducing food.

The average apple of three-inch diameter contains 125 calories; an apple's fruit sugar content is between eight and eleven per cent. Two apples add to your eating as many calories as a three-inch veal bird. The apples are bulky, of course, and satisfy your hunger as a single veal bird cannot do, but they are by no means to be left out of your calorie counting.

We eat apples, of course, for their taste. It may be that the copy writer who invented the slogan about the apple and the doctor spoke the truth. The high Vitamin C content of the apple and the liberal amount of fruit sugar it contains surely make it a wholesome food. I doubt, however, that anybody's health is greatly improved if he eats this great fruit merely as a medicine. If he eats it for enjoyment, on the other hand, his body will not rebuke him for giving it this wholesome nutrition and his general sense of well-being will be nourished, too, by his pleasure. If he happens also to be reducing, his quiet conscience will give him peace of mind for seeking satisfaction in the low-calorie apple instead of some higher-calorie or larger-quantity appeasement of his hunger.

There are many apple adventures to be had. Besides eating them as they come from the tree, try a compote of Rome Beauties cooked with tangerines, a little butter and a little sugar. Make an apple and orange salad by combining Stayman apples with Baldwins, nectarines, and Florida oranges, extending the juice with a little canned or frozen orange juice if necessary. For dessert, choose large apples (Rome Beauties again) to bake, and flavor them with a little red wine or Kentucky bourbon, lemon juice or buttermilk. Do you know that apple sauce can have quite a variety of tastes according to the mixture of apple varieties you put into it? Are you aware of the many recipes that call for blanching apples in sauces made with different wines?

A friend of mine perfumes the raw apples he eats with a few drops of applejack or of the well-aged French applejack, Calvados. The slightly wooden taste of the cask in a Calvados that is very old combines wonderfully with a fresh, crisp taste of raw apples, and a few drops make so little calorie difference that even reducers can enjoy this added touch.

Apples have been interesting to great eaters for two thousand years. Cato, the conscience of the Roman Senate, wrote of the different varieties of apples that grew around ancient Rome. There is not one of the great French cooks who did not win added glory with some recipe for a new apple delight. In England they sell their great apples, the Blenheim and the Cox's orange pippin, displayed with highly polished skin on a cushion of cotton. The French diner honors the first *reinette grise* of the season by paying exorbitant prices for it in restaurants frequented by leading gourmets.

Gourmets all over the world have complained in recent years that the dollar shortage of their countries has prevented them from enjoying the many American apples they had before World War II, which they considered the finest apples grown anywhere. As the dollar shortage subsides, Slim Gourmets will again be able to recognize each other across the seven seas, eating a good apple for dessert or a snack, calling it by its correct name and tasting it with the respect this great gift of nature and great friend of the Slim Gourmet deserves.

24 EASY WAYS TO GREAT SOUPS

Language preserves many good old customs. The French word, *souper*, and the English, *to sup*, remind us that soup used to be the main dish at dinner. Today the soup has been relegated to a minor but still important role. It is the overture to a good dinner, the curtain raiser of the Slim Gourmet's most important meal.

"The Slim Gourmet's? Aren't soups fattening?"

This question has been asked of me so often that I think it is time to save the honor of the soup, one of mankind's greatest inventions and warmest comforts.

Soups can be fattening. So can oranges. If you eat mindlessly and don't know what you are eating, anything can help you to assemble excess weight. Two bowls of a thick lentil soup with frankfurters and ham may cost you 1,200 calories, even more, if an economical cook pours all the leftovers of the refrigerator into the pot. But that is not merely a soup. It is what the Germans call a *gedraengte Wochenuebersicht*, a condensed survey of the week.

On the other hand, a generous bowlful of a tasty split-pea bouillon with onions counts for only 85 calories, the equivalent of a less than medium-sized apple. It was prepared by two of the great soup cooks of the world, two rivals who often work together harmoniously in our kitchen. One is Mr. Heinz, the other Mr. Campbell, and the co-ordinator who contributed the browned onions happened to be our cook. It took her no more than seven minutes of light work to produce this gourmet's delight of a soup.

This is one secret of the Slim Gourmet's inexhaustible treasure of great soups: the simple recognition of the canned soup wizardry that we can buy for very little money anywhere in this country.

There are few first dinner courses so satisfactory to the majority of diners as a well-prepared soup. It can be had at little expense of either cash or calories.

Soups are not only a gourmet's delight. They are also recommended by nutrition-wise doctors. The cheer that emanates from a good soup quickly appeases the appetite, prepares the palate as well as the stomach for good food to come, and gently puts the complicated mechanism of the digestive apparatus to work.

After the soup, we are no longer sharply hungry. We are out of danger of thoughtless gluttony and can easily be content with our personal portion size of the courses that follow.

A good consommé (46 calories) is difficult to prepare. The perfect chicken soup (74 calories) is a rare achievement. For a few dimes we can have both and we can also mix the two cans and obtain a chicken consommé (60 calories) which combines the strength of the beef consommé with the flavor of the chicken soup. You add, perhaps, some chervil. I add a bay leaf. Taste is a personal matter. Why should not soups be our individual creations?

A light dinner may begin with a heavier soup: a plate of potato soup (162 calories) with some chives; a potato-julienne with leeks (135 calories); perhaps a mixture of cream of mushroom and bouillon (110 calories).

There are hundreds of ways to compose soup poems if we take canned soups as our raw materials and invite our ingenuity to blend, to season, to create. Once we have learned about soups, their variety, their nutritional value, their caloric differences, we will eat them without fear. We will include them in our menus even while we are reducing. We will use them to *help* us reduce. A good soup at the beginning of a meal is a pleasure in itself and a safeguard against overeating of any kind.

While I was reducing, my soup plate was regularly only three-quarters full. My family are soup devotees. Our soup mixtures are famous. It would have been foolish to deprive myself of these creations. But I could be satisfied with a little less soup than the rest of the company, and I could thus save 11,000 calories during a year's time—three pounds of surplus weight divested by the simple means of a three-quarter helping of soup. A marked measuring cup in the kitchen was a reminder to the cook.

A good observer would also notice that our creamed mushroom soup is different from the soup he has at home. It is a mixture of canned cream of mushroom soup, which all by itself costs 200 calories a plate, and consommé—35 calories for a full plate—saving calories and improving the mushroom soup besides, especially if tarragon and chopped chives are added. The calorie count of the new and delicious result is a mere 118 per full plate.

There are soups and soups, even on the calorie chart. A creamed tomato purée counts for 90 calories, gumbo Creole is 100 calories, and clear consommé is 35 calories. The non-creamed split pea soup counts only 150 calories and French onion soup without the cheese and toast is 150 calories.

That's not so bad. Most soups can easily be eaten out of my Martini allowance.

There are great soup recipes in all cookbooks. Many don't need such high-calorie ingredients as oil or butter, chicken fat or cream. In one cookbook I found more than 170 different recipes for beef consommé alone. That did not include the clear fish soups, of which this book provides another twenty-two, twenty game consommés, and more than 140 chicken consommés.

There are discoveries to be made in foreign lands and in foreign cuisines; many are being welcomed today into American kitchens. We have assimilated the oxtail soup from the British, *bortsch* from Russia and Poland (there are two kinds, of which the Polish is lighter and the Russian a meal in itself). We can try our luck with the *bouillabaisse* from Marseille or the Russian fish soup *ouka*, which is more digestible, the German beer soup, or the Italian minestrone, which is more useful when we want to reduce.

The French *pot-au-feu* we will choose for a real *souper*; it is a one-course dinner. We might attempt Hungarian goulash soup when the other courses on the menu are very light.

Perhaps your personal taste leans toward the home-grown soups. How many chowders do you know? There are others you haven't tried. Boston and Manhattan are not all of America, and if codfish can go into a soup with bacon, so can clams with asparagus. There are numerous fish chowders, and vegetable chowders without either fish or shellfish. There are Yankee bean soup and southern gumbos and many fine regional soups worth discovering.

When you have graduated through the canned soups and the cookbook soups to creative soup invention, there is every reason to predict that you will refine your dinners and your figure by eating soups without fear.

But you already know enough to soup well and reduce. Here are a few Slim Gourmet soup suggestions that cost 150 calories or less for a plate:

SOUPS—150 CALORIES (OR LESS) A PLATE

Bouillon	10	Creole gumbo	100
Tomato bouillon	30	Chicken with rice	100
Consommé	35	Tomato and rice	125
Tomato soup	75	Chicken gumbo	150
Chicken broth	75	Vegetable	150
Beef broth	100	Oxtail	150
Noodle soup	100	Split pea soup	150
Chicken noodle soup	100	French onion soup	150

25 THE SALAD INVENTOR

IN THE KITCHEN

Around 1795 a penniless French aristocrat earned his living as salad mixer for wealthy New Yorkers. Today, 160 years later, many New Yorkers could teach the world how to prepare salads.

Americans have a garden of salad greens and fresh vegetables in which to browse the year round, in the vegetable markets of almost any town or city. Californians, living in sunshine, have taught us how to combine the products of their orchards and their irrigated valleys in the salad bowl. Avocado and citrus fruits, raw vegetables and flaky fish or shellfish, fruits with a sprinkling of nuts—the variety of salads one can put together for good eating is almost unlimited. Every American woman in her kitchen is her own salad inventor.

The only imperfection in the American salad civilization is the use of too many, and too heavy, creamy, or otherwise taste-overpowering dressings. A dressing that is too self-assertive shouts down the delicate flavors of the ingredients. Fish tastes like fowl and beets like cucumbers.

Monsieur Pierre, the headwaiter of a distinguished New York restaurant, gave me an extraordinary lesson in salad invention. He unites two food-loving nations by the very circumstances of his birth. He was born on the S.S. *DeGrasse*, a French liner that voyaged the Atlantic from 1890 to 1920; at the moment of his birth his sea-going birthplace had sailed past the Statue of Liberty and so he is a Frenchman born, but born in New York. Talking food with him, you discover at once that this native New York Frenchman combines the best of both worlds: American daring and freedom from traditionalism, and the French taste for food and love of good eating.

We became kindred spirits when I protested against over-shadowing the taste of an asparagus salad with French dressing. He offered to prepare for us a salad à la Pierre.

Into a large bowl he put a good dozen of asparagus spears cut into small pieces, the chopped whites of two hard-boiled eggs, finely hashed olives, and the diced half of an apple. Mixing the whole, he sprinkled it with about a tablespoon of a very dry California white Napa wine, and the salad à la Pierre was born. It tasted like spring itself, and its 160 calories were an added satisfaction to the Slim Gourmet.

The next day I went again to Pierre's. This time I wanted a substantial salad lunch. He proposed a shrimp and chicken salad. Here is what he did:

He cut a slice of toast into little pieces and soaked them for a while in a mixture of two tablespoons of dry sherry and a dash of French cognac. Then he added the diced white meat of two chickens, fifteen halved shrimps, a cup of small cooked peas, a few slices of celery roots and a head of shredded crisp lettuce. He mixed it thoroughly, and we had such a meal as never before, satisfying and light as a lunch should be. And it counted only 370 calories per person. A wedge of American Camembert cheese with a cracker and a cup of French-roasted black coffee put a period to a perfectly composed lunch. The entire meal was 440 calories, and a great eating experience besides.

I asked why this salad was not printed on the menu card.

"Because it did not exist when you gave your order," he answered. "One does not make the same salad twice. It is composed out of what is available in season and quality. I just today had these wonderful chicken breasts and an especially fine head of lettuce."

Pierre's secret is one the home salad inventor already knows: a salad is invented fresh on the spot. You may find it in your refrigerator, as Pierre found the breasts of chicken, or you may put it together as you stroll through the market. The season, the day, the crates of produce that arrived fresh that morning, all contribute to your salad.

When the choice ingredients are themselves the inspiration of the salad, who would be misled into quenching their flavors with a heavy dressing? Especially to followers of the Slim Gourmet, the taste is the joy. Why should we spoil our pleasure with an over-spiced dressing, and add calories to the salad besides?

I have eaten salads of Pierre's with a mixed dressing now and then, but he uses them sparingly, with respect for the good things he has put into the salad bowl. His preference is to sprinkle a few drops of wine, whisky, or liqueur, sometimes a little oil, once some buttermilk. When young cauliflower was on the market he made a salad of cauliflower with anchovies and tomatoes touched up with a whiff of bourbon. The principle he taught me is that the dressing should always be secondary, the salad ingredients first. The dressing is no more than the background of the portrait, the piano accompaniment of the song.

In this country everyone in his own kitchen can be a great salad chef. Pity the diet faddists, to whom a salad is not exquisite food but only a grim last stand on the calorie barricades—a few lettuce leaves, a spoonful of cottage cheese, and perhaps they dare squeeze a drop of lemon juice (I cannot bear even to mention the abomination of mineral oil dressings).

Fortunately they have not succeeded in spoiling the joy of salads for the rest of us. As an adornment to a meal or a meal in itself, the imaginatively filled salad bowl is the delight of the Slim Gourmet.

26   REDUCING ON EGGS AND

SLIMMING ON SOUFFLÉS

Ten soft-boiled eggs, plus toast and butter and marmalade and coffee, were former King Farouk's breakfast. "Farouk explains, 'I like eggs,'" the story was headlined. In the Slim Gourmet's opinion it would be reason enough to depose a king merely for the barbarism of repeating the taste of an egg ten times until the palate is numb to its yolky softness and the just-firm texture of the white.

If the subject of this story had been someone more admirable than the insensitive and overweight successor of the Pharaohs, I would have shown him how a lover of eggs can relish this exquisite food even more while at the same time losing five and one-half pounds in a year by simple egg arithmetic.

Almost everyone eats eggs in some form and most of us find them the most satisfying part of our breakfast. A boiled egg counts for 70 calories, but of these 70 the white represents only

14, the yolk 56. While I was still a stout gourmet looking for the way to slimness, I charted my eating habits and found that my average of two cherished eggs a day added up to 730 eggs, a total of 51,100 calories, in a year.

Since no chicken farmer has yet managed to produce low-calorie eggs, I began an egg-calorie reduction scheme of my own. My eggs for breakfast were boiled as usual. Only, when eating the egg, I left out half the yolk. When I ate them scrambled, my serving contained two whites and only one yolk. The same simple subtraction is easily performed with omelets and most other egg dishes by using half as many yolks as whites. The half-yolk eggs give the same taste, the same satisfaction— with the difference that during my reducing year my 730 eggs counted only 32,860 calories instead of 51,100.

These 20,000 calories saved on eggs reduce the reducer five and one-half pounds in a year even if he does nothing else to reduce but only eats no more than his body needs (in other words, he stays within his maintenance calorie allowance).

As for the second half of this chapter's promise, I believe I am the first reducer who can report indisputably that he has reduced successfully on that queen of egg dishes, *the soufflé*.

During the seventy-eight weeks of my reducing there was not one week when I did not eat at least one soufflé, whether I was at home or abroad, in Caracas or Milan or London. There were many weeks when my eating was enhanced by two or three soufflés on my menus. They did not interfere with my reducing. On the contrary, they helped, making my meals rich and delectable and my calorie consumption light.

I discovered the soufflé's unique place in a reducing program with the help of two people separated by centuries as well as geography. One was the priest who became famous because he dined one day at five o'clock instead of six and thereby allowed Brillat-Savarin to discover *the omelette du Curé*, the tuna-fish "omelet of the priest." The other was a diet designer in California.

The best-known omelet in literature, which Brillat-Savarin composed of tuna and carp's milt, counts 210 calories. On the day I figured this out, I read in a diet article the Californian's ardent propaganda for skimmed-milk cottage cheese as the regular basis of one's diet. One cup of this wholesome food, he pointed out, contains only 200 calories.

With all respect for cottage cheese, I vote for the priest's omelet. With all respect for wholesome food with little taste, I prefer fine dishes with great taste.

It came to me then that there was no reason why the greatest of egg dishes should not be part of a reducing program. The most refined and most versatile, the most eye-appealing and most taste-pleasing of dishes, the soufflé, might well become the Slim Gourmet's permanent companion.

There were dozens of soufflés stored in my memory's treasure chest as great taste experiences: the chocolate soufflé at home that gives luster even to an improvised meal; a lobster soufflé at the celebrated Plaza Athenée and another I had eaten in 1951 at a Paris railway station restaurant; the asparagus soufflé of Mrs. P. in Newark; the spinach soufflé which Gertie perfected to make her children accept this wholesome vegetable, and Tibby's soufflé *au Grand Marnier*. I remembered soufflés with shrimps and soufflés with calves' liver and tomatoes, fish and ham and cheese and onion and tea and coffee soufflés, soufflés with strawberries and peaches and rum and whisky, and even a beer soufflé I ate once at a Belgian gourmet's house.

Most American cookbooks contain from ten to forty recipes for soufflés; the French *Larousse Gastronomique* offers seventy-five. If we could adopt the soufflé as a dish for the Slim Gourmet's reducing, we could banish boredom forever from the table and introduce a lovely culinary diversion from our daily enjoyment of natural tastes.

Soufflé as a reducer's companion? Is it not too difficult for the average homemaker? Does it not demand the most refined kitchen wizardry?

The purported difficulty of making a soufflé is a myth that has been exploded by all authorities. A soufflé is a simple performance, provided only that there are more egg whites in it than yolks (put the soufflé at the top of our list of reduced-egg dishes). The whites raise the soufflé without any help, and all goes well if the eaters wait for the soufflé and the soufflé waits for no one, not for latecomers or laggard eaters or the thoughtless guest who talks with the serving spoon in his hand until the soufflé sinks into its shoes.

I have known many cooks and housewives who never dared to attempt a soufflé because it was supposed to be so difficult. Once they tried they were surprised to see how easily they succeeded.

Another myth about the soufflé has been propagated by the carrot-stick diet designer. "Soufflés are fattening! Think of the butter, the cream, the many eggs—oh, the calories in a soufflé!" The word "fattening" no longer shocks the Slim Gourmet, who knows that even oranges can be fattening and an occasional candy is an aid to slimming.

We need not generalize. We can refute the diet designer with his own favorite weapon, and give a few calorie statistics on the original soufflé recipes as they are printed in some American and French cookbooks.

We see that there are soufflés that count 200 calories per portion, a great majority between 200 and 300, and some that soar to 900 calories.

The 900-calorie recipe need not alarm you. It will not sneak up on you in your own dining room or even in any restaurant you regularly frequent. You can mark it down now for the time when your reducing target has been reached and you find yourself in Paris. Until then, you can safely forget the celebrated lobster soufflé of the Hotel Plaza Athenée.

Should you want a lower-calorie lobster soufflé while you are in Paris, you can have even that. Monsieur Viaux invented it and serves it in his restaurant at the Eastern Railway Station (Gare de l'Est). It has 400 calories and is one of the choicest eating pleasures in my memory.

A superb asparagus soufflé counts around 200 calories per portion. So do most vegetable soufflés, and a mushroom soufflé is even less. A chicken liver or cheese soufflé is between 250 and 300 calories. This is the average calorie count of most of the soufflés that can be served as a main dish: shrimp, clams, fish and chicken, turkey, kidney, veal, and beef.

The dessert soufflés—chocolate, strawberry, liquors, tea, coffee, and so on, count between 250 and 400 calories. I have eaten a peach soufflé that was a poem and cost me exactly 230 calories.

Nutritionally, soufflés rank high as wholesome and balanced eating. They are rich in proteins. If you vary your soufflés—eating now a cheese soufflé and next time ham, another day spinach, chicken breasts, strawberry, apple—making use of the wide variety of soufflé bases which the cookbooks provide, the different soufflés in your menus week after week will give you a good balance of all the vitamins and minerals essential for healthy eating.

The soufflé as a reducer's companion has a psychological subtlety all its own. It is next to impossible to overeat on a soufflé. As a main dish it is voluminous to the eye; light as it is, it fills the plate. For its approximately 250 calories it offers a generous gift of pleasure and taste. And—subtlest of all benefits —there is no danger of a second helping. By the time you are ready for a second, the soufflé has gone. Either it has all been served or it has become a flat shadow of its original splendor. Soufflés are made to be eaten immediately after they leave the oven.

A shrimp soufflé (250 calories), a mixed fruit salad (200 calories) and a wedge of Camembert cheese on a bit of toast

(170 calories) make a delightful dinner. Accompanied by a glass of good dry white wine (70 calories), this agreeable meal costs not more than 700 calories altogether.

If you can reduce this way, why live on carrot sticks?

27 DON'T EXTRACT

YOUR SWEET TOOTH!

Of course we can live without sugar. A good part of the human race seems to have done so until the sixteenth century, and even in the seventeenth sugar was sold at a high price and only in pharmacies as a sort of medicine. We could also live without the automobile and the washing machine but who wants to?

Great Britain has given us an example of what happens when sweets are forbidden or restricted. As long as sweets could be bought freely by everyone, the yearly consumption was seven ounces per head of the population. Rationing created a hunger for sweets and today the Britishers eat eight ounces per person.

No sweets during a diet lead to too many sweets afterward. That human nature will triumph at last over food taboos has been demonstrated over and over. I myself can testify to the truth of it after my seventeen diets. So can almost any diet victim.

The biologist can prove scientifically that we need much less sugar than we eat. The sugar contained in fruit, he tells us, is sufficient for our body's needs. A candy before a meal is for most people an efficient appetite stopper. Parents try to prevent their children from eating sweets too soon before a meal because sweets do not take the place of a balanced diet.

All this is true. But it is nevertheless my experience that nothing is gained by suppressing a craving for sweets. Fighting against one's strong appetites is a hard job and rarely rewarding, however irrational those appetites may be, whether their origins are nervous or emotional or psychological or in some quirk of the body's chemistry. It is better to tame them with kindness than chain them with force.

A chocolate bar costs 250 calories, and the question to ask is only whether one can afford it. I find a hamburger more satisfying for the same number of calories—in my better moments. But do I buy rubbers when I long for a bright new tie? Does the lady of the house buy bed sheets when she craves a spring hat? Our emotions and even our thinking do not follow strictly logical lines. Frequently I settle for a compromise. Hard candy is calorie-cheaper: an ounce costs only 100 calories and often satisfies my craving for sweets. The knowledge that I am a free agent and can do what I like helps particularly. I did not fall victim to the chocolate temptation more than ten times during my seventy-eight weeks of reducing. Thus I spent about 2,500 of approximately 1,000,000 calories a little less sensibly. Did it really matter? Would it have been worth while to fight my craving and fill my heart with envy, anger, and self-pity for the sake of those ten chocolate bars?

The sweet tooth can be a problem for habitual sweet-eaters. It was a serious hindrance to reducing for little Sylvia, who gobbled up half a pound of candy a day—1,300 calories. A blanket ban on sweets did not stop her. Her mother gradually helped her to eat less by teaching her to enjoy her candy more. It took more than six months to accustom her to eating only three candies a day—and eating these for taste and conscious enjoyment. She still loves candy but now she enjoys its taste and no longer stuffs it unconsciously as a consolation and a reaffirmation of her little personality struggling to assert itself. Her mother helped her, too, by giving her sweets of another kind, the extra love and attention she seemed to need. Many of us, adult though we are, might try to learn how much of our craving for sweets is really a craving for more subtle comforts. It is possible that by discovering what we really want when we long for sweets, we can find a more direct way to satisfy our emotional hunger—and save ourselves the excess pounds.

Many a sweet tooth develops in childhood because candy is offered as a bribe for good behavior. "If you finish your carrots you may have a chocolate cherry—" This makes carrots a chore and puts a premium on candy. The active child may not become too plump on sweets but the way to future overweight is often unknowingly prepared by parents in this manner.

The craving for sweets may come from tension, from boredom. At times the body or the blood seems to need a little extra sugar; science has not yet told us exactly why.

For all these reasons it is wiser to control an occasional craving for sweets than to fight it. Sweets in moderation are easily built into a reducing program without endangering the calorie allowance. They will not be enemies of the reducer, unless he tries to extract the sweet tooth with violence, and bans sweets from his life by a sweeping decree. Then the appetite for them lies in wait, gaining strength, and ambushes him when he is least prepared.

An intelligent lady I know, experienced in dieting, had denied herself all sweets for six weeks or so. Her diet was otherwise well balanced though severe. She wanted to lose twelve pounds and was making steady progress—until one day, alone on a train, bored and weary, she beckoned the magazine vendor. She bought not only a magazine but also a bar of chocolate. It was a huge bar, the only size the vendor had. She thought she would eat one square. By the end of her journey a few hours later she had eaten the entire bar. Sick at heart as well as at her stomach, she had not the courage even to count the calories.

What no-sweet dieter has not had a similar experience? I had, more than once, during my dieting days. It is the unfulfilled wishes that are dangerous. If our intelligent lady had treated her sweet tooth a little more gently, if she had taken a candy once in a while and counted it in her calorie budget, it would not have set a trap for her.

The sweet tooth can be an aid to reducing. A candy now and then can forestall a binge of overeating. A small dish of ice cream for dessert once or twice a week during reducing prevents a great guilt-producing sundae.

Don't try to pull out your sweet tooth. Deal with it considerately and you will be safe from sneak attacks. Chocolate is a delicious invention. Take a piece you can count in your budget, nibble it, taste it, savor it slowly and fully. It will cheer you on your Slim Gourmet way.

28   THE SLIM GOURMET

ENJOYS HIS DRINK

Your waistline may be in direct proportion to the size of the glasses you buy for your home bar.

The praises of wine have been sung by poets through the centuries and its virtues extolled by philosophers. Some do not share this enthusiasm for the cheering glass, and for them it is unnecessary to read this chapter. For a great many, however, the drink before dinner, the highball in the evening, the wine at table for festive or perhaps for ordinary occasions, are a pleasant adornment to living. Some must drink at business luncheons or cocktail parties. Some do not drink otherwise, but pour themselves a beer and another beer while they are entertained by television.

The calories in alcohol are a worry to many, and this has come to the attention of the alert gentlemen who write advertising. They tell us to drink one beer rather than another because the first has fewer calories. Because rye has 170 calories to the jigger and Scotch only 150, must we drink only Scotch? But suppose one does not like Scotch? Should we read the label according to the "proof" (by which we can count calories) and buy accordingly? Where then is the pleasure in a drink? If it is not enjoyable, why drink at all?

The Slim Gourmet does not take such a grim view. He believes that it is not necessary to change from one drink to another only because it has fewer calories. There are good reasons for not limiting one's enjoyment of drinking to one kind of whisky or one kind of beer, but the difference in calories is not one of those reasons.

For example, I prefer Cuban to Jamaican rum; it is milder and of superior taste. That it has only half the calories of Jamaican rum is a dividend to my enjoyment.

The good reasons for change have to do not with calories but with enjoyment. We can conserve our calories in a much more simple way and without sacrificing enjoyment.

Let us consider first the calorie aspect of drinking. This is not higher mathematics but only the simplest arithmetic. I have said at the beginning of the chapter that your waistline is in direct proportion to the size of the glasses in your bar. In the restaurant or the public bar the glasses are usually smaller than they look. At home they are usually larger than they look. In the matter of glasses there are many optical illusions. Their bottoms may be solid, or hollow, or partly solid and partly hollow. A curved inner bottom may make the glass seem to hold more or less than it actually does.

How do you pour whisky? Do you fill a jigger, pour it into the glass, and rest content? Or do you, like most of us, look at it after you have poured a jiggerful, and add perhaps half a jigger or three-quarters, or perhaps pour from the bottle until it looks like enough? The jigger is an exact measure, with a specific number of calories. But the glass is full of sly deceptions even to the experienced eye. Do you know how many ounces your glass holds? Even if you do, do you know how many half-jiggers you have added to make the glass look invitingly filled? In the restaurant or bar, when you order your drink on the rocks you are served the rocks in your glass and the whisky in a pony. It makes a difference.

So your first exercise in bar arithmetic is to know the size—the actual size in ounces—of your glasses. Your Old-Fashioned glasses may be four-ounce or six-ounce. For highballs you may have ten- or twelve-ounce glasses. You may be using a pony to measure, which is less than one ounce, or a jigger, which is about two ounces. The barman expects to get eighteen highballs out of a fifth of whisky. How many drinks do you get out of the bottle when you are pouring them?

At home, when you are the host, you may be as generous as you like with your guests' drinks, but you are not obliged to match them drink for drink. If you have been accustomed to taking a jigger of whisky for yourself, take a pony. If you pour according to the glass, use a smaller glass for yourself.

As guest, you can watch your host pour your drink. (Even better, the Slim Gourmet thinks, is self-service at the bar.) There is no law against asking him in advance to pour you only one jigger, or one pony. You can nurse your one drink indefinitely, sipping it for taste. One who really enjoys his liquor does not gulp it down. Gourmets are not given to drinking in quantity.

At a bar, take your drink on the rocks, with a bottle of soda and a separate glass if you are thirsty.

Drink your beer in a wine glass. Your normal glass of beer holds the contents of one bottle or can, 12 ounces. When you have filled your glass three times during an evening of television or conversation with friends, you have consumed 36 ounces (500 calories). With the same expenditure of energy in pouring, your wine glass filled three times gives you the pleasure of your beer and you have taken only 12 ounces (167 calories).

When you have wine with dinner, use your good wine glasses —but fill your own glass only one-third full. To enjoy the wine, you do not need quantity and the mere repetition of the taste. You only need to taste the wine you have, slowly, savoring it to the full.

Whatever size glass you have been using for your own drink, from now on use the next smaller glass.

And that ends the mathematics of drinking the Slim Gourmet's way. The rest is not science but art.

Even more than with eating, we drink for pleasure. Let us concentrate on the pleasure. Let us not drink whisky or wine or beer to quench simple thirst. Let us drink water for thirst, and the more interesting beverages for pure enjoyment.

How shall we enjoy our drinks more so that we can drink less? It is very simple. We *taste*. We drink slowly, sipping—*tasting* what we drink. We buy and order better quality for the pleasure of taste. We buy and order variety for the interest it brings to our palate.

When you buy, consider with your liquor dealer some of the finer, more expensive varieties. There is a psychological effect about a higher price and a more distinguished label. Automatically, when you drink your well-aged bourbon or rye or your liqueur Scotch, you will drink it respectfully, slowly, for taste. You will not pour boldly from the bottle, but measure it out with care.

This is not stinginess. This is how a gourmet shows his respect for the quality of what he drinks. This is the tribute he pays to the skill and experience of the distiller, the brewer, the vintner. This is the honor due to an old and mellow friend. To pour it carelessly, to toss it down at a gulp, does both yourself and the fine drink a disservice. Your English host serving you his oldest port, your French host pouring you his best cognac, would be shocked if you drank it down too quickly, even though he had many bottles to spare in his cellar. Your Southern friend who brings out for you a fine bourbon put down in his grandfather's day would be wounded at your hasty, thoughtless swallowing. Most of us today do not have a cellar, and few of us live in the same houses our grandfathers lived in, but we can still show our respect—and savor our enjoyment—with a really fine whisky or wine or beer.

When you buy these finer qualities, though they are surely more expensive, you will find that your calories will go down, your enjoyment will go up, and your liquor bill will stay very much the same.

As you cultivate your taste for finer quality, you will find also that you are cultivating your taste for less sweet drinks and more dry ones, for fewer mixed drinks and more straight ones. I have seen both these trends developing in the United States over the past ten years. In the Soviet Union today they are drinking *Koktels*; they are only now beginning where Americans were in the 1930's at the end of Prohibition. Today Alexanders and Pink Ladies are less frequently ordered or offered, few people remember what is in a Bronx, and the Martini, while becoming more popular, becomes steadily drier and drier.

The straight drink and the dry drink are generally preferred by the cultivated taste. Happily, it is also a fact that the straight drink and the dry drink contain fewer calories than mixed and sweet drinks.

Variety is your next step in the enjoyment of drinking. Whatever you like to drink, whether it is whisky, wine, or beer, you can enjoy many new tastes by going on the search for variety.

I had been in the United States for some years before I discovered a distinctly American distilled liquor called applejack. My American friends were reluctant to offer it to me; they were rather scornful of it. Yet the moment this apple brandy was labelled Calvados and its cost was doubled, my friends considered it very fine. The main difference between the applejack from

Normandy and the applejack from New Jersey is age. The French discovered that this fine liquor is even finer when it is fifty, perhaps a hundred, years old. Americans only drink it too young.

The same is true of port. Americans buy the best port, but they drink it too young. In England when a son is born to one of the old families, two things are done: The child is entered at Eton or Harrow, whichever school is in the family tradition. And port of that year's vintage is put down in the cellar. When the young man marries and sets up his own household, his port goes with him. He is not likely to begin drinking port after dinner until he is forty or forty-five. By that time the port, being of the same age, is well mellowed. I have drunk port seventy-five years old with a gentleman celebrating his seventy-fifth birthday. Such admirable customs are not, perhaps, for the twentieth century. We must find our own ways to develop fine old wines and liquors.

Applejack is so little regarded that it is still generally available from small local sources. If you have such a source, cherish it. Applejack is a good drink before dinner or after. It goes admirably with a fruit dessert. It is as versatile as cognac in its way.

If cognac is part of your drinking vocabulary, try some others besides the French. There are also very good Greek and Portuguese brandies, often far less expensive; a fine quality can be had for little money. They are of the same general flavor as the French. The California brandy is also good though different, and can give you another taste pleasure.

Whiskies have a whole scale of taste pleasures to offer. There are Irish, rye, bourbon and sour-mash bourbon, which is different again, and a great variety of Scotch whiskies ranging from moderate to the very expensive Glenlivet, the unblended Scotch; a very little in a small glass is a special treat.

Beer is much too good a drink to be drunk like water. Your local brew is probably the least expensive in your area, but it may become routine and you are perhaps drinking it automatically, without tasting and without real enjoyment. Include a little interstate variety with your beer, and sometimes perhaps an imported brew like the Mexican or Dutch or Danish beers, the Canadian or Irish ales.

A young wife I know bought her husband for Christmas a case of a variety of beers, American and imported. The gift gave him great pleasure at the time, and the pleasure has continued. He relishes his beer now as a fine drink and probably he will never again gulp it thirstily without tasting.

Another friend, a physician, likes to entertain a guest from another city or another country by serving him a beer from his own home; it is a thoughtful bit of hospitality and at the same time the doctor himself enjoys a great variety of beer tastes.

Wines have been treated with so much mystery and ritual that many who would have pleasure in drinking wine are discouraged from trying. In the province of Burgundy in France I once had a trout freshly caught in the innkeeper's brook, with a red Burgundy wine from his cellar, made by himself from the grapes in his own vineyard. To him it was not a question of what wine to drink with fish. He drank the wine he had, offered it to his guests —and it was superb.

Jellied trout in red wine is a famous gourmet dish. We cook delicious lobster dishes with port wine or Burgundy. And on the next page the cookbook contradicts itself and tells us: "With fish serve only white wine!" The wise gourmet obeys his own taste.

The wine charts also are often open to question. Vintage years are a useful guide but not an infallible one. I have had many a good wine from a much maligned year. The French wine waiter in a good restaurant often recommends a bottle from a year which is not recommended by the wine charts. You can generally trust him.

An artificial wall has been raised around wine drinking in a country like the United States where wine is not an old familiar friend. In France every peasant is a judge of wine. As vineyards develop in this country, Americans too may cast off their shyness and make their own choice of wines without consulting the wine charts. We hear only about French wines, read about them in the magazine articles and books about wine. Out of ten writers on wine, nine speak only of French wines and only one, perhaps, of California wines. Every little French vineyard has been written about, but of the Napa Valley in California we do not even see a photograph.

It is true that some California wines do not travel well; by the time they reach Chicago or New York they are no longer very good. The same is true of many little French and Italian wines that are delicious on their home soil but do not go to Paris, and surely not across the ocean. Some, mistakenly, do attempt the trip. I have been disappointed in New York by more than one French wine that I have enjoyed in France.

Patriotism will not make us drink a California wine because it is American. We will drink it only if it is better wine. There are quite a few that are better than European wines. We cannot put our trust in a label. We must taste and find out for ourselves.

When you drink wine, if you are only two at the table who are drinking, don't open a big bottle because then you will be tempted to finish it so as not to let it stand open. Many good wines come in half bottles, the right amount for two.

Many times throughout this book, as in many good cookbooks, wine and liquor are suggested for cooking. This is nothing to fear. In the cooking the alcohol (with its calories) cooks away and only the taste remains, an enhancement to the dish.

On the whole subject of alcohol, many studies have been made on the good effects of a little wine or whisky. Doctors often prescribe a drink for relaxation and for quick energy, especially at the end of the day's work before dinner. There are also, of course, those who oppose alcohol in any form.

To the wise, too much of anything is not good. The Slim Gourmet sees an actual loss of pleasure in the automatic lifting of a glass to the lips. The pleasure of drinking is something to be cherished. The Irish painter Jack Yeats, whose brother was the poet William Butler Yeats, ends his working day at four and from four until seven o'clock he entertains his guests with sherry. After dinner he drinks Irish whisky. This is his way of enjoying his drinking and it suits him. As I write this he is eighty-four years old. When we entertained him at a hotel, I asked the wine waiter for a very good sherry, and mentioned that Mr. Yeats was coming. The sherry that was brought was the finest, smoothest, mellowest I have tasted. But when I tried to buy several bottles for myself they were not for sale. They were kept only for Jack Yeats. He cherished his pleasure in drinking, and he drank the best.

It is a good rule for those who set out to become Slim Gourmets.

29   NO TWO RECIPES ARE ALIKE

The proprietor of the celebrated Italian restaurant suggested *fettucini* (noodles) *all'Alfredo*, a wonderful idea for a one-dish luncheon even for the reducing Slim Gourmet. I ordered it for memory's sake. Years ago Alfredo himself had prepared it for us with elegance and dexterity, in his renowned place in Rome. I wondered how it would taste when reproduced in New York.

The fettucini came, and with it twelve pats of butter, eight ounces of cream, and a full cup of grated Parmesan cheese. I added quickly: 1,300 calories of ingredients plus the 200 of the noodles did not sound like a Slim Gourmet's luncheon.

"Do you have to use all that? Alfredo in Rome uses much less, if I remember rightly," I said to the waiter.

"Yes, Sir, but our guests like to see a more thorough performance."

"I cannot eat so much. Would you mind making mine with one-third of the butter and cream—the cheese I will add myself."

The "reduced" *fettucini all'Alfredo* cost me only 600 instead of the usual 1,500 calories offered to the unwary diner, and tasted much more like the Roman original than what the waiter was prepared to mix at my table.

I was still wondering about this strange transformation when I reached home in the evening. What had brought about the change in Alfredo's recipe on its journey from the Tiber to the Hudson? Are ingredients so unimportant in the Italian kitchen that they can be doubled or tripled without concern for the eater's enjoyment, health, and digestion?

The cookbooks I consulted did not contain Alfredo's fettucini. I compared other dishes, however, in various American and foreign cookbooks and thus I discovered another source of overweight where I least expected it. The ingredients—butter, lard, wine, and salt pork—which three well-known cookbooks specified for *boeuf à la mode* or French pot roast differed per portion between 130 and 310 calories. This means that in one portion of this popular dish you can eat either 380 or 560 calories—a considerable difference!

Once awakened, my curiosity led me to further research. I pored through eighteen authoritative cookbooks. I found that a cheese omelet in one recipe counted for 300 calories, in another 550. A portion of Southern fried chicken might be 400 calories or 700. A chicken curry in one cookbook required four tablespoons of butter; in another, six; in still another, eight. One recipe asked for one-third cup of butter for a soufflé; a second demanded one-half cup, and double the flour and double the milk.

These were not diet cookbooks which thin down famous dishes and often sacrifice taste on the altar of calorie-saving. The cookbooks I compared were all normal kitchen guides for home-makers and professionals, written with only one goal in mind: better cooking for more delicious eating.

The diner trying to follow his calorie chart is rarely in a position to take these differences into account; he scarcely even knows they exist. The homemaker in her kitchen is hardly aware of them. But the Slim Gourmet must know that there are differences among recipes if his reducing is to succeed. He is also interested in comparative recipe research for another reason: what in a dish determines the taste? Must not different ingredients or different proportions produce different results?

The Slim Gourmet's predilection for natural taste suggests a guiding principle: he will prefer those recipes that concentrate on the main ingredient, and list smaller quantities of whatever secondary ingredients are used.

One cookbook alone obviously cannot give the cook different versions to compare so that she can arrive at a happy balance. This is one reason why we have added a second and a third and many more cookbooks to our kitchen shelf. (Another reason is, of course, the Slim Gourmet's constant search for variety in new and different dishes.)

Any kitchen where cooking for better eating is practiced needs more than one cookbook in order to match recipes against each other and modify them successfully. This comparative recipe research is moreover a liberating experience. With not one, but several, experts to guide us we can experiment more confidently until we find the recipe that agrees best with our own palate.

Recipes do not make good cooks. Cooking is a creative art. It asks us to improvise, adapt, and improve upon what others have invented.

Comparative recipe research teaches us that no recipe is sacred. It is only a script for the play that the good cook directs in his or her own domain.

Of recipes there is no end today. The average bookshop offers a choice of thirty or forty cookbooks and every year dozens of new ones are published in the United States alone. The United States Government Bureau of Home Nutrition has published hundreds of recipes; the popular magazines abound with recipes on both editorial and advertising pages. Food packages are adorned with alluring recipes, and their manufacturers offer booklets of them on request, even whole cookbooks. Radio and television and the food pages of the newspaper acquaint us with often excellent advice on how to improve cooking and eating, and give us recipes as well. If we compare our present food knowledge and eating habits with those of only twenty-five years ago we must admit that our food editors and cookbook publishers have made a remarkable contribution to our eating.

But there can be too much of a good thing. The flood of information, advice, and especially of recipes, is likely to swamp us. It becomes harder and harder to know the good from the bad, the proven and sound advice from the promotional recipe that aims mainly at selling a particular food.

The Slim Gourmet has an additional concern. Recipes and cookbooks often neglect natural taste, extolling rich sauces and cocktailized foods. Or they fall into the error of most diet cookbooks and measure by calories instead of taste.

So all our cookbooks are full of red, blue, and green pencil marks. There are notes in all the margins, and many NO signs mark the blackballed dishes that have been found wanting.

The proof of the cooking is in the eating. In eating we acquire judgment by experience. Followers of the Slim Gourmet's way make their own recipe digest, selecting from the mass of recipes those that are tastiest, most natural, least difficult to prepare, and lowest in calories without sacrifice of flavor.

30   THE GOURMET BROUGHT

UP TO DATE

"The kitchen is the only food factory." "No manufactured sauces." Thus read two of the maxims of the Club of the 100, the French society of the elite of gourmets.

Nobody doubts that a gifted cook after hours of toil may succeed in making a better chicken soup than those I can buy ready-made at the supermarket. Let us by all means forbid the use of cans and prepared foods by cooks whose profession it is to prepare and create great dishes for us when we go to a temple of eating and are able and willing to pay the check. But what can these antique gourmets' rules mean to the millions of modern gourmets who want to eat well and have other things to do besides "simmer a round steak for four hours"?

Spinach to that, says the Slim Gourmet. He believes it is more admirable to serve forty million families a good oyster stew (out of a can) than to serve a hundred or even a thousand gourmets a very, very good one which takes four hours of work and an inspired chef. There are only a few kitchen geniuses in this world and I prefer to have them cook for the supermarkets and their millions of customers rather than for Lord Rothschild and his select circle of guests.

Monsieur Point, who owns one of the best restaurants in the world in Vienne, France, makes a few thousand guests a year smack their lips and revel for decades in the memory of his savory food. But I think the unnamed composer of Campbell's Vichyssoise or Heinz's Madrilène is a greater benefactor of humanity, serving millions of us with great soups that nine out of ten cooks could never reproduce.

There are a few cooks deserving of fame who can make a better mustard than we can buy from Grey-Poupon of Dijon, or beat a more mouth-watering mayonnaise than Hellmann. How many? No more than a hundred in the United States. No more than a thousand in France. Are the rest of us condemned forever to products of our own labors because the guardians of a traditional gastronomy pontificate against the food-processing industry?

The Slim Gourmet's is a twentieth-century eating philosophy. It makes no objection to well-prepared, time-saving products of industry. Their honesty and purity is attested to on the label, thanks to the United States Government. They only need to taste good!

We are seeing enacted with food the same comedy we lived through with furniture, with clothing, even with medicines. Not so long ago it was still a common prejudice that ready-to-wear clothing was inferior to the custom made, and that any cabinet-maker in one's home town was superior to a manufacturer in Grand Rapids. I remember a British medical officer who tried to convince me in 1943 that a packaged medicine was less effective than a pharmacist-made prescription.

Today that British colonel's life may be saved by some packaged aureomycin. Americans are better dressed in their ready-to-wear suits than the Dutch or the Irish, who cling to their custom tailors. Grand Rapids now mass-produces designer furniture for millions of homes and the days are forgotten when the only alternative was to collect Sheraton of doubtful ancestry.

An airline advertises that on its New York-to-Paris flight the dinner that is served is made to the recipes and directions of the cooks of Maxim's, one of the great Parisian restaurants. To me this advertisement opens wide vistas for the future. The time is not far when the frozen food industry will hire the great master cooks at high salaries and thus initiate a new era in our eating. We are barely at the beginning of this development, and even now New Yorkers can buy in some food stores a real bouilla-baisse made with Mediterranean *langouste* and *rascasse*. Tomorrow we may all eat Monsieur Point's food poems in our homes, made according to his recipes, supervised by his master cooks, and produced at prices that everyone can pay.

The Slim Gourmet has witnessed the death of the fine tradition of home preserving in Great Britain, and yet sees it survive in the jars of British jam manufacturers. Today they export all over the world delights that fifty years ago were still a privilege only of the British landed gentry.

Brillat-Savarin said that the invention of a new dish is a blessing to humanity. So is the launching of a new can or frozen package and its intelligent use in the home. Of course there are good and there are bad foods on the market (as there were always good and bad cooks in home kitchens). There are good and not-so-good ways of using manufactured foods.

We learn how to distinguish a good prepared food and how to use it for better eating. But that deserves another book.

31   THE SLIM GOURMET'S BREAKFAST

"A good cup of coffee, a fresh roll, and golden butter" was the modest ideal breakfast of a hotel owner in a Southern resort, who nevertheless offered his guests eighty-four suggestions from blueberry muffins to porterhouse steaks on his breakfast menu card.

Herr B., a vintner of Traben-Trarbach, drank beer for breakfast, as did the English of the fifteenth century, and the Columbus Hotel in Miami, Florida, dispatches its guests with an Early Bird breakfast of coffee, orange juice, and doughnuts when they must make a dawn plane connection.

There is no ideal breakfast for everyone because our morning moods and habits vary so widely. There are people who take their breakfast half asleep and still dreamy and others who wake up full of energy and with a robust morning appetite. There are the throat-clearing uncommunicative husbands who separate themselves from sunshine and family by a newspaper wall while putting away a hearty breakfast, and chatty wives who peck at fragments of toast because they are simply not hungry in the morning. There is an army of commuters who gulp their coffee as they fly and there are breakfast addicts who make it the most delightful meal of the day.

My Chinese neighbor breakfasts in summer on a cup of tea served in paper-thin china on a beautiful tray with a rosebud in a silver vase, while his British guest eats fishcakes, or a kippered herring that asserts its presence all too emphatically on the morning air.

The Slim Gourmet's is a tolerant philosophy. It respects the most individual morning moods provided they do not exclude the mind from breakfast enjoyment. The hasty 8:11-catcher who is too busy spending his few breakfast minutes with the front page headlines to know whether he is drinking coffee or tea is no breakfast ideal. Nor is the dieting matron who skips breakfast for her figure's sake.

The Slim Gourmet's breakfast is built on the three *F*'s, the basic grammar of any sensible breakfast: fruit, food, fluid. He offers one vital suggestion: Change your breakfast menu every day.

There is a simple reason for this advice. The most exquisite food becomes boring when it is repeated too often. We get used to it, no longer relish the taste, don't put our minds into our eating—and we overeat. I have never understood why people always eat eggs in pairs. The Slim Gourmet, who enjoys the taste of an egg, does not need the taste repeated. If he eats his boiled egg on Monday, cheese on Tuesday, ham on Wednesday, chicken livers on Thursday, oatmeal on Friday, sausage on Saturday and an omelet on Sunday, his breakfast can never become routine and he will not eat it absent-mindedly.

Whether you eat fruit as a first or last course of your breakfast is a matter of personal choice. Eat it whenever you like it best and choose the form in which you like it most. Grapefruit is a delightful breakfast fruit but to eat half a grapefruit every morning of the year kills its delight. With breakfast fruit it is especially rewarding to follow the seasons; thus you achieve variety and also eat the fruit you like at the peak of its taste.

It may be an iced cantaloupe or a tomato, cherries or fresh blueberries. It may be an orange or sliced banana, peaches or an apple, gooseberries or a pear, red currants or grapes, mango or papaya, raspberries or apricots, plums or pineapple or one of the four hundred fruit salads out of the *Salad Book* of the Edgewater Beach Hotel.

Or you may drink your fruit, pressed fresh or frozen or canned, preferably without added sugar. The mixing of commercially available fruit juices—grapefruit and pineapple juice, for instance, or prune and lemon—will bring additional variety to your breakfast table and an imaginative touch to your menu composition.

What fruits do you particularly like? If you have been taking your fruit first at breakfast all your life, see how you like taking it in the middle, with cold cereal perhaps, or last, as dessert. For your reducing period choose the low-calorie fruits and fruit juices among your favorites for a more generous helping now and then. Of course you will not eat four or five bananas or drink pineapple juice in twelve-ounce glasses. Slim Gourmets do not indulge in jumbo portions.

Leave out the fruit you don't like, no matter how low in calories or high in vitamins it may be. Nobody will force you to eat anything that is not on the list of your food desires. If the food you enjoy also enriches your system with minerals and vitamins, of course you will not object. But we think first of the mouthwatering joy of a cup of fresh blueberries, or a well-ripened cantaloupe on which we sprinkle a few drops of lemon juice, and satisfy our conscience afterward with the scientific fact that we have improved our health with ten to fifty milligrams of vitamin C.

Has the fruit whetted your appetite? It is time to eat something more substantial. If the main dish is to be the Southern hotelkeeper's roll and butter, we will take care to obtain a fresh crisp roll, and butter that does not resemble an ice cube, coming fresh from the refrigerator, but is soft enough to taste. Or we may have French bread, or rye bread one or two days old. The Slim Gourmet has a different kind of bread every day, and usually two kinds on the plate; he likes to keep his awareness of the bread's own taste, so easily lost through frequent repetition.

If you like cereals, try to eat them with as little adornment of sugar and cream or milk as possible. Don't submerge the oatmeal, making it an excuse for the cream. Use the cream as an improvement of the oatmeal's own taste. Cold cereals combine well with many fruits. Puffed rice with fruit salad is a heartening breakfast dish. Shredded wheat with strawberries does not need sugar; ripe strawberries have their own sweetness.

You may like a slice of ham or beef tongue, bologna sausage or cheese with your breakfast. During your reducing period you will need to watch that this slice does not use up too much of your calorie allowance for the day. This is even truer for the devotees of griddle cakes who like to eat many of them with generous helpings of maple sirup, for doughnut and sweet-roll addicts, and those who are fond of French toast. These foods are Mount Everests of calories. The usual helping of griddle cakes can easily amount to 600 calories—that makes quite a dent in your calorie allowance and may endanger your reducing plan. Yet the Slim Gourmet would not advise you to abstain from griddle cakes altogether, even while reducing. There is a way to include your favorite in your plans.

Breakfast enjoyment and reducing go best together when the breakfast menu changes every day. In case you have dangerous flirtations with waffles, griddle cakes, doughnuts, muffins, and other high-calorie breakfast delights, a weekly plan permits you to indulge in your high-calorie predilections one day a week. Let us assume that you allow yourself 400 calories for breakfast every day. If for six days of the week you use only 300 calories a day, you can then on Sunday morning eat your four griddle cakes with maple sirup without endangering your program of losing a pound a week and becoming a Slim Gourmet.

One winter I followed this system during the whole month of December, in preparation for spending my Christmas vacation with dear friends whose Christmas ritual includes very rich breakfasts. During the seven days from Christmas to New Year's, I knew I could use up 700 calories at breakfast every morning instead of my usual 300 calories. These calories I saved from November 28 onward, cutting down my breakfasts by 100 calories a day, a not too difficult task.

When the time came for griddle cakes and waffles, muffins, doughnuts, Spanish omelets, French rolls, and bacon with eggs, my table companions wondered how I continued to reduce while participating in the family's non-diet breakfasts. The secret is out, now, for the benefit of readers who are subjected to similar temptations.

Many diet books prescribe plain cottage cheese as a main dish for reducers at breakfast. I have often wondered how many dieters obediently eat unadorned cottage cheese every morning. To the Slim Gourmet cottage cheese is a raw material to be made into something. How many different dishes can you make out of cottage cheese? In the spring I like it with fresh cucumbers and chives, bound with the addition of a little buttermilk. In the winter it makes a wonderful bread spread when mixed two parts to one with India relish. In the south of France I was once served a combination of cottage cheese, hard-boiled whites of eggs, and tomato ketchup, a delicious dish that was no stone on the conscience of any reducer.

Inventing a new breakfast dish every day is a challenge to Slim

Gourmets. Like a good musician who has faithfully played the scores of composers and enjoys improvising for his own pleasure, Slim Gourmets who have followed the cookbooks with receptive minds and palates also like to improvise. The good taste of food is their guide. The improvisations of creative eaters as well as creative cooks become recipes and family traditions and give new eating pleasure to others besides the inventor of the dish.

What do you drink at breakfast? The British like their early morning tea and used to have their first cup an hour before breakfast. A similar tradition among Southerners in the United States was to wake up to a cup of fragrant black coffee. With the pace of the twentieth century this leisurely custom is vanishing both in England and in the United States.

My own preference is a well-brewed cup of black coffee at the end of my breakfast—not too hot. The difference between coffee too hot and coffee just right is perhaps only a degree or two but one numbs the palate and the other can be tasted.

I do not have to have coffee every day. I can also have tea, and not the same tea every day. One day it is smoky Lapsang Souchong and another day a blend of Assam and Ceylon teas, particularly refreshing in summer. Then I may drink a Chinese Ichang tea or one of the light Earl Grey teas that have become popular with the many tea-drinking Americans.

Some time ago we tried consommé for breakfast and found that a hot consommé or bouillon is a wonderful breakfast drink. We alternate it with coffee, tea, and milk, to banish from our breakfast table the boredom that makes taste buds sleepy and eating mechanical and dangerous.

"Breakfast is a beautiful season," they say in Switzerland, where a whole nation breakfasts on coffee with milk, rolls, butter, and jam. It is a much more beautiful season in the United States, where millions enjoy individualistic breakfasts. Breakfast is the beginning of a new day and a good breakfast frequently influences the course of the day.

Whether we come in a good mood to our daily work, strong

and fresh and healthy, or arrive still grouchy and full of evil fore-bodings, depends to a large extent on whether we master the gentle art of breakfast menu making. The essence of this art is to find the middle way which to the Chinese philosopher Confucius was the heart of philosophy: the middle way between our body's needs and our palate's desires, between eating too little and eating too much, between being too much and too little concerned with our comfort and happiness.

32   THE SLIM GOURMET AT LUNCH

The light lunch is far from a new invention. The men of antiquity knew only two meals, which the Greek translators of the Bible called *ariston* (the morning meal) and *deipnon* (the evening meal). A few olives, a piece of bread, a little wine mixed with water, was all that the ancient Hebrews, Greeks, and Babylonians ate at noonday. They took their breakfast after hours of work around ten or eleven o'clock in the morning, and dinner in the afternoon between four and six o'clock when the day's work was done and they could enjoy a leisurely meal.

The French still call their luncheon *déjeuner*, which means breakfast, and the coffee-and-roll breakfast *petit déjeuner* or little breakfast. The four-course, alcohol-punctuated lunch habits of our days are not agreeable to the Slim Gourmet. He likes a hearty breakfast but a light meal at midday. Only on Sundays, when no work interferes, can he take his main meal around noon and enjoy it fully.

Hearty breakfasts plus heavy luncheons are often a reason for overweight. It is easier and more wholesome to cut down on luncheon than on breakfast. A light luncheon is moreover in tune with present-day American eating habits. People who work know from experience that their afternoon duties are easier after a light midday meal than after a heavy one. Even at home a sandwich or salad has replaced the noon dinner in most urban households.

Even in this country, however, many professions, habits, and family traditions lead people to eat more richly at lunch than at dinner. Some actors and doctors, journalists and housewives, farmers and ranchmen like to take their main meal in the middle of the day, and the Slim Gourmet sees nothing to complain of in the custom, provided the meal can be taken in leisure and relaxation.

Hasty eating is often thoughtless eating, and that is bad and fattening, whether you have a light or a full luncheon. A sandwich with coffee and pie at the office desk is a sin against health and mental balance and a crime against good eating.

By a long overdue declaration of eating independence, fresh fruits, original and tasty salads, seafood and omelets, are on the way to replacing the sandwich in the American luncheon. The sandwich for lunch is one of the most harmful heritages that England bequeathed to her American colonies. Not the Black Plague nor Napoleon nor the Spanish Armada, to my mind, was England's historic enemy, but the fourth Earl of Sandwich, who gave his name to a health-destroying eating habit from which their common sense and self-interest have not yet liberated the British people.

Every day at lunch hour one can watch the office population of London storming the thousands of little sandwich counters in the City, at the Strand, in Victoria Street and Oxford Street, munching without time or joy the mountains of sandwiches that are prepared every morning of tasteless bread, watercress, egg, and cheese. It is a pitiful example of mindless, animal eating, and I hold that the sandwich is mainly the cause of it.

It seems to me that the fourth Earl of Sandwich was not even the inventor of the food device for which he is given credit. What we call the sandwich probably comes to us from the eastern shores of the Mediterranean, where the Arabs today still eat their *pita*, a flat round bread, by filling its "stomach" with olives or a relish of some kind. Some food experts ascribe the invention of the sandwich to the great Jewish teacher, Rabbi Hillel, who originated the Passover ritual of sandwiching between two pieces of matzos some bitter herbs and a relish made of nuts and grated apple mixed with wine, as a reminder of Hebrew sufferings before the exodus from Egypt.

The Slim Gourmet's opposition to the sandwich stems from the taste-killing effect of the two slices of bread. What is sandwiched between them becomes completely immaterial. We get only an inkling of the taste of the eggs or lettuce or ham or cheese or whatever garnishes our sandwich. It is obvious why, after their sandwich, so many at the luncheon counter order ice cream or a piece of pie—they want at least to enjoy their dessert. This whole procedure takes about ten minutes, fills the stomach without pleasing the palate, and involves a consumption of 700 to 900 calories.

The sandwich against which I inveigh is the one both floored and roofed with bread. I do not breathe a word against the two hundred special "sandwiches" which the famous Danish eating place, Davidson's, offers under that misleading name. They are unroofed, and so ingeniously composed that our drugstore kings would do well to send expeditions to Copenhagen for Mr. Davidson's recipes. I still treasure the memory of an evening in his tiny restaurant when we experienced so many delicate and surprising tastes that we soon stopped noting down what we ate and took home his whole six-foot menu card.

A little of Davidson's rich choice at least would be worth imitating at the drugstore counter or restaurant if it were feasible. A list of only ten sandwiches limits the choice and imagination of the average eater so that he develops an affection for one or two which he eats day after day.

The Slim Gourmet's light luncheon is not a sandwich nor is it a one-course luncheon. Three courses of small quantities of food are the Slim Gourmet's choice. Reducers do well on two courses, either an appetizer and a main dish or a main dish and a dessert. Observation has taught me that it is advisable to start with an appetizer and skip the dessert. Otherwise the waiting period may be too long and there are always the rolls, butter, and knife to tempt the reducer to use up calories he does not wish to spend in this way.

During the reducing period, the first course can be a fruit juice or fruit salad, tomato or vegetable juice, a madrilène or other clear soup, clams or oysters, a shrimp cocktail, celery and olives, or whatever fresh fruit there is in season. To begin luncheon with a bunch of grapes is quite customary in certain parts of southern France. Apart from being most delicious, grapes offer occupation for nervous fingers and stop us from playing with that roll and butter.

All these first courses cost about 100 calories, no more.

If for economic or other reasons the main dish of the luncheon has to be a sandwich, any sandwich can be rendered more civilized by the simple removal of the top slice of bread so that the contents of the sandwich have a taste. If lunch hour and lunch money allow, there is a wide choice of luncheon dishes which combine high nutritional value with low calorie counts. Here are some that will cost no more than 300 to 400 calories: a seafood platter of shrimps, oysters, scallops, crabmeat; a lobster, either cold with a very little mayonnaise, or broiled, or steamed (this last is the best—steamed lobster can be ordered in any seafood restaurant and cooked at home from the recipe in any good cookbook); and, of the fish with scales instead of shells, broiled lake trout or brook trout, Boston scrod, red snapper, or pompano.

For non-ichthyophagists (people who don't like fish) eggs in various styles make an ideal luncheon. A well-made plain omelet is a perfect light midday meal. Or the golden fluffy omelet can be dressed with *fines herbes*, diced ham, a little cheese, tomato, shrimps, or chicken livers. Soft poached eggs on spinach are light and not more than 250 calories even if two eggs are your personal portion size.

At a business luncheon or a club luncheon meeting a mixed grill, broiled breast of chicken, or calves' liver made with bacon and eaten without it are good choices for reducers.

Veal cutlets or grilled sweetbreads, beef tongue or a hamburger, one frankfurter with sauerkraut, and of course all kinds of steaks, ribs of beef, boiled beef, or roast beef, if eaten in small personal portion sizes, do not make a luncheon too heavy. To the beef-eaters the Slim Gourmet's advice is to leave out the dessert. A good main dish is enough of a good thing for luncheon.

Of vegetables, a reducer is wise to choose cauliflower, asparagus, spinach, or stringbeans, sometimes stewed tomatoes, broccoli, or carrots, and about once in two weeks a small baked potato.

If you happen to be a salad lover, the problem of a light luncheon is solved for you. Almost every cookbook gives a recipe for the so-called chef's salads, which also appear regularly on most restaurant menu cards.

There are vegetable salads that satisfy the most educated tastes. In Italy I learned how to make a salad of cauliflower, asparagus, celery root, and cucumbers, with the white of hard-boiled eggs and a Gasconne dressing made of mustard, chopped garlic, a little oil, a little vinegar, and a crust of bread rubbed with garlic. Back in the United States, I added half an avocado to this combination and, on festive occasions, a few shrimps.

As a dessert for Slim Gourmets at lunch I recommend cheese, a different kind each day eaten with a different kind of bread;

half a slice of bread or half a roll is sufficient. There are dozens in every supermarket and a few to choose from on most menu cards. A delightful new cheese was recently added to our cheese vocabulary: the NuWorld cheese, a creamy and yet crumbly whole milk cheese of a pale yellow color, which was discovered by chance in the School of Agriculture of the University of Wisconsin.

Cheese gives your light luncheon the perfect finishing touch. Of course, if you have not had fruit at the beginning of your meal you can end with a slice of honeydew melon or cantaloupe, a pear or an apple or, in season, berries without cream. If others are having ice cream you might like a sherbet; half the regular restaurant portion is a reducer's personal portion size.

A drink at luncheon? My own preference is to save my enjoyment of a drink until my day's work has been done. If your calorie allowance permits, half a drink might be just enough at lunch time.

33 THE SLIM GOURMET'S DINNER

The occasion was an anniversary. The dinner was exquisitely cooked, perfectly served, but the hostess was mortified. The guests had left half of her beautiful dinner untouched. Here was her menu:

Smoked salmon was the first course.
A consommé with noodles was second.
Then came lobster Thermidor (with cheese sauce).

Duck with oranges and pineapple and all the trimmings.
Spaghetti with almonds accompanied the main dish.

and we ended with:

Angel cake Melba
Fresh fruits
and coffee.

The surprising fact about this anniversary dinner, which
would have cost me 3,500 calories if I had eaten all of it, was that
it was too much for everyone. Forty years ago it would have been
considered quite normal. I am sure many famous New York restaurants of that day, like the Lafayette or Sherry's, maintained
many similar menus and even bigger ones.

Our ideas of what a good dinner should be have changed, and
quite naturally so. Knowingly or not, we take into account our
many labor-saving machines and a way of life that costs us com-
paratively little physical energy.

Dinner comes at the end of the day and should be the crown
of it. But the crown need not be oversize! Whether we are alone
or in company, dining at home or out, receiving few guests or
many, with the exception of a four-hour wedding feast, more
than three courses are too much of a good thing for twentieth-
century hosts and guests.

Appetizer, entree, dessert? We need a new terminology. The
Slim Gourmet believes that everyone must be free to follow his
own habits and eating wishes and plan his meals according to
his own taste. Thus the appetizer will be rejected by many who
do not feel they have dined if a dinner has not begun with a
soup. Others do not consider either appetizer or soup essential;
they prefer a conversational drink before dinner with a variety of
hors d'oeuvres. Still others prefer a fruit or fruit juice. Only a few
insist upon beginning their dinner with what might be called
an appetizer, and even these not all the time. All these varied
tastes can find what they like under a new heading, *overture*.

Now the second or main course. *Entree* is an obsolete word. In the old French cuisine, which regularly served more than one main dish at dinner, it was used literally to mean the *entrée* or entrance of the several main courses, beginning with the first one. In this country, since we normally are content with one main course, *entree* has come to mean that course itself. To call this an *entrance* when there is none to follow seems to me paradoxical and meaningless.

I prefer *opus*, which means *work* and is used mainly for works of art. That is what the main course should be: a work of art.

The third course I call *divertimento*, an Italian word that is used for a light, entertaining piece of music. Whether we choose fruit or cheese or a savory or even a salad, or sometimes what might accurately be called a *dessert*, I do not want to decide arbitrarily. The choice depends on the personal tastes of the hosts and guests, the habits of the house, and what goes well with the preceding dishes. To call the last course a "little piece of music" protects us from making it a heavy-going chore at the end of dinner.

While the structure of our dinners is much lighter today than it was at the beginning of this century, their composition is another question. We have many more choices than diners of the past. Transportation, refrigeration, and deep freezing have all but abolished both geography and seasons. We do not eat strawberries or fresh green peas only when they grow in our own part of the country. The whole strawberry-producing and pea-growing world sends its products fresh to our markets and if we cannot have them fresh we have them frozen or canned.

Can you remember when we ate oysters only in the months with an R? When those who lived away from the seacoast had only the fish from nearby lakes and streams and no salt-water shellfish at all?

One would expect that this technical development had wonderfully enlarged our food vocabulary, that the dinner menus would be much richer in variety than they were fifty years ago.

But are they? Of thirty-one dinner parties we attended in New York during the winter of 1953-54, the main course at eighteen was turkey, six served chicken, four had roast beef and three offered duck.

Furthermore, the eighteen hostesses who gave turkey dinners used without exception the same recipe, which I enjoy thoroughly at Thanksgiving but less and less from December to March. The chicken dishes were much more entertaining; they at least were prepared according to a variety of recipes. I shall not forget the chicken fragrant with sweet vermouth—every guest took home the recipe.

My menu statistics, however, do not reveal a wide food vocabulary among New York hostesses even in the mid-twentieth century of faultless food storage and food distribution. Where were the saddles of lamb, the shashliks, the beef tongues, the tender cuts of veal that lend themselves to the most exotic taste blends? Why was there never a lobster, why no salmon or shad? Has fish disappeared from the American table? We must try not to be guilty of such monotony when we come to the composition of our own menus!

Calling the main dish not entree but opus reminds us to begin our planning with this, the principal work, and arrange the overture and the divertimento so that the three form a balanced and unified composition. The dinner composer should also not forget that at the mid-point of the twentieth century a dinner ought not to contain more than 800 to 900 calories. Rich dinners always embarrass at least one member of the family and one or more of the guests who take their weight seriously. It is not a happy experience to sit at a too heavily laden table and apologize for not overeating.

Now that we have all assembled, refreshed ourselves and perhaps relaxed with a drink, we go, full of expectation, to the dinner table. Our overture tonight is a double consommé made of equal parts of veal and beef consommé. The veal broth gives the consommé a slightly jellied character and brings the tastes of the two meats to full flavor. A few noodles make the clear soup visually more interesting (our eyes must enjoy eating, too) and do not add materially to the calorie count of this light and delicious overture.

Here comes the main dish. This week there is fresh asparagus on the market and asparagus is the main theme of our opus this evening. It appears in all its spring glory, to be eaten "natural taste," flanked by two kinds of ham—smoked ham and Virginia ham—and sliced smoked tongue, and there is a specially made asparagus relish of finely chopped egg whites and parsley bound together by hot butter. The portion sizes are such that we do not eat ham with asparagus; we eat asparagus, with the various meats as complementary flavors.

The divertimento tonight is something we have never eaten before, a salad composed especially for this occasion, of pears, apples, celery, grapes cut in half, quarters of oranges and tangerines, and lettuce. The dressing is the hostess's creation: experimentally she mixed a little sour cream with brandy and pernod; this French liqueur permeated with its anisette-like fragrance not only the sour cream of the dressing but all the fruits that went into the composition.

The salad is the climax and we all eat generous helpings. We could eat generous helpings of everything this evening and still remain within our 900-calorie dinner maximum. Our tastes have been charmed, our eyes pleased, and our reducing desires not disappointed.

For a family dinner many homemakers are in favor of the one-dish meal. They believe that one eats less and loses weight if there is just one dish and no choice. This is contrary to my experience and that of most observers. The less choice there is on the table, the bigger the portions and the more second helpings.

On another evening we have guests. They come rather late and therefore there are no canapés with the drinks before dinner. They go hungry to the table—but they will not have to wait. On each plate there immediately appear six Bluepoint oysters on the half shell, and dinner begins as soon as we are seated.

Tonight we are conventional. We found a wonderful sirloin steak and here it is, unaccompanied by any green vegetable, because it is peppered and peppered steak kills the taste of a delicate vegetable. It comes with only one companion, a medium-sized baked Idaho potato. On the table are bottles of imported Dutch beer and the wine glasses in which it is to be served, true to Slim Gourmet tradition. What special flavor do you notice in the steak? Yes, it is cognac. One minute before it was served, the steak was sprinkled with a good old French cognac that pleases our nostrils and enhances the flavor of the meat.

The menu planner is weight-conscious and a good calorie accountant. The male beginning of this dinner, however, asks for a very feminine counterpart. Here it comes fresh from the oven, a delight for expectant eyes, the soufflé Rothschild, a soufflé flavored with kirsch liqueur and blended with finely chopped crystallized fruits, just enough fruit to look well but not so much as to infringe upon the aroma of the kirsch that rises from the still liquid center of the soufflé.

With the coffee we serve snifters of the same kirsch that went into the soufflé. It refreshes our taste memory and ends the dinner on a note of harmony.

Use any calorie counter you like: even if you took generous portion sizes of every course, the maximum you ate tonight was 900 calories.

Is it so difficult to reduce on such fare?

34   EATING MUST BE MARRIED, TOO

The husband and wife with the same taste in food and the same eating personalities do not exist. The word "we" is rarely used when married couples discuss their food likes and dislikes. It is mostly: "My wife eats salads but she gives me steak," or "I don't care for pies but my husband adores them."

Many wives wonder why their husbands remain slim and trim while they become round on the same foods. The answer is simple and obvious. People learn to eat as individuals. No one has yet taught us how to marry each other's personal eating ways. Until we learn how to eat "together," we cannot really be happy at the dinner table and our figures and possibly our health are likely to suffer as the result of a conflict of food personalities.

Mrs. R. wrote from her home in a southwestern city that she gained weight fast while her husband, eating exactly the same, kept his youthful figure.

Mr. R. was a native of New Orleans, Mrs. R. from New England. He liked southern food: fried chicken, hot biscuits, stuffed red snapper, pecan pie, and all the delicious gumbos and casseroles of Louisiana's rich food lore. Mrs. R., far from the clam chowders, the Boston scrod, and the red flannel hash of her youth, loved her husband, served what he liked, ate what he ate, and gained weight at a frightening pace.

She was happily married except in her eating and did not even know that this was the reason for her weight problem. She had sacrificed her food personality on the altar of marital bliss, and gained in return overweight instead of peace of mind. With a lack of joy in eating the meals she composed, prepared, and cooked only to please her husband, she ate quantity instead of quality. To keep any hint of her discontent from spoiling her husband's happiness she ate every scrap on her plate. In two years or so of marriage she had gained twenty-five pounds and could not stop gaining.

She was always going on a diet, losing ten or fifteen pounds rapidly and gaining it back in short order. Eating at the family table is the end of almost any rigorous diet. To diet one must really give up all social eating and withdraw to munch alone like an animal in a cave gnawing a bone. This is hardly a way to keep a marriage happy.

The better way to reduce in Mrs. R.'s case or in any marriage is to be tolerant in menu-making not only to her husband's, but also to her own food personality. The better way is to "marry" husband's and wife's food habits, designing a new family food personality that has room in it for both members.

In all other respects we know that marriage means a loving give-and-take between two individuals with many differences. But we take it for granted that these two persons of different sexes and sizes, different backgrounds, different working and living habits, can eat the same dishes, portions, foods, and menus, day in and day out. In many cases marriage stops at the table. The family's meals are composed without thought for the different needs and different wishes of its members.

A quick way to discover how far apart in eating ways a man and wife can be is the restaurant test. The next time you eat out, make the test. In restaurants people usually order what they like most; many order what they cannot get at home. So will you. So will your husband. Compare what you ordered, where you agreed and ordered the same, where your orders— let us say, tastes and desires—parted. Then you can try to answer some questions: Why did your husband order a steak and you fried liver? Is it because you never dare to have fried liver at home since he dislikes it? He ordered cheesecake and you no dessert. Do you eat sweet desserts at home against your inclinations? Does he prefer a certain restaurant because there they cook "just like Mom"? Do you choose a seafood plate because fish is banned from your table?

Eating out reveals an obvious truth: Every man, woman, and child has a food personality of his own. There are rarely two people with identical eating habits; perhaps identical twins come close to it, although even of that I am not certain, but surely husbands and wives do not. We need to accept the difference as a fact, study where we are different and "marry" our eating as we have married other aspects of our living.

The French talk eating with delight. Americans more often talk about reducing. Did she follow the Hollywood diet, the hostess asks her guest. No, Mrs. Jones answers, she followed the new caloric, mineral, high protein, low pleasure diet that was just published. Follows a description of the ounces lost and pounds regained and this goes on at millions of dinner tables. Sometimes it is the wives, sometimes the husbands who make conversation of their weight problem. And this is another difference that needs to be married: rarely are both husband and wife concerned with their weight. It is always one or the other.

Food is something worth talking about. It is much more entertaining than the temporary starvation of Mrs. Jones who seems to have sat next to me at every dinner party since calories were invented. Unless it is Mr. Jones, one place farther down the table, who has the weight problem in the Jones family. Whichever it is, both are unhappy.

That marriage often leads to overweight is an old observation and a common experience. Why it should be so has never really been explored. There must be many reasons, but one of them surely is that husband and wife, however well married they may be in other respects, have not married their eating. One or the other is bound to suffer.

Husbands and wives will have to talk eating when they propose an eating marriage to each other. The aim of marriage is a happier life. That is also the purpose of the eating marriage. Both partners become richer if they become masters in the art of adaptation. The husband's vacation dream is the sea, the wife's a mountain resort; both will be happy at Lake Constance. A marriage of eating follows the same general principle. It is important that you talk about eating together and explore and come to know each other's eating personalities. If you know each other you can blend your personalities into a gracious eating marriage that gives both of you joy in eating.

The compromise between no broccoli and no asparagus may be found in an occasional artichoke. The way out between boiled potatoes and French fried may be a baked potato with three pats of butter for the thin partner and one for the reducer. The mayonnaise conflict can be resolved by serving mayonnaise separately so that each decides at the table whether to take much, little, or none at all. There are men who never eat a dessert but love to start a meal with a fruit salad or half a grapefruit. In married eating, one can eat the fruit at the beginning and the other at the end of dinner and both are happy.

No more examples. The fun is to work out your eating marriage as you work out your happiness in other aspects of marriage, all by yourselves.

An old philosopher said that the greatest danger in married life is taking each other too much for granted. How much do you really know about each other's eating likes and dislikes? Here is the Slim Gourmet's Eating Marriage Quiz to help you find out. Answer the questions separately, and then compare your answers.

A. WIFE'S QUIZ

1. Do you know whether your husband prefers sweet desserts to cheese or fruit?
2. Do you know what fruit juice he likes best?
3. Does he like coffee the way you make it at home?

B. HUSBAND'S QUIZ

1. Do you know whether your wife prefers sweet desserts to fruit or cheese?
2. Do you know what fruit juice she likes best?
3. Do you know her favorite drink?

4. Do you know whether he prefers soup or an appetizer?

5. Do you know more than 3 dishes his "mother used to cook"?

6. Do you know 3 cheeses he likes?

7. Do you serve occasionally (but not exclusively) dishes he loves and you dislike?

8. Do you eat your main meal together?

9. Do you breakfast together?

10. Does he often choose in restaurants dishes you serve at home?

4. Does she allow you to give her order in restaurants?

5. Do you know more than 3 of her favorite dishes?

6. Is hers a better kitchen than your mother's?

7. Do you know 3 desserts she likes?

8. Do you enjoy home eating more than eating out?

9. Do you from time to time suggest a dish you like?

10. Do you tell her when you like what you are eating?

SCOREBOARD

Ladies and gentlemen, score the YES *answers in your quiz:*

A. WIFE'S ANSWERS	B. HUSBAND'S ANSWERS
1. _____	1. _____
2. _____	2. _____
3. _____	3. _____
4. _____	4. _____
5. _____	5. _____
6. _____	6. _____
7. _____	7. _____
8. _____	8. _____
9. _____	9. _____
10. _____	10. _____

YOUR EATING MARRIAGE IS:

HAPPY — if together you scored more than 14 points.

IN NEED OF
IMPROVEMENT — if you scored between 7 and 13 points.

IN VERY
BAD SHAPE — if you scored between 0 and 6 points.

35   THREE GREAT TABLE COMPANIONS

OF THE SLIM GOURMET

Some foods recommend themselves to the Slim Gourmet only for their taste. But some give double value: their taste is unique and superb, and their calories are low. Three of these have become the Slim Gourmet's great table companions: the onion, the artichoke, and the asparagus.

Moses, Cleopatra, and the Empress Theodosia have been variously credited with discovering onions for the Western world. Egypt and Palestine are said to be the original homes of this uniquely flavored vegetable that appears on our tables today as onion, leek, or shallot.

I have eaten them in both their home countries, but I must confess that Egyptians and Israelis alike have a great deal still to learn from the French, who have liberated the onion from its kitchen slavery and elevated this child of the Middle East to greatness in the vegetable kingdom.

They have exported their most famous onion dish, French onion soup, to our shores, and American kitchens have welcomed it from coast to coast. Creamed onions, French-fried onions, and the Italian onion pizza have also become naturalized Americans. And yet I believe that the onion is still not sufficiently recognized in this country as one of the finest, tenderest, and most wholesome vegetables available to us.

Have you ever eaten an onion soufflé with a broiled steak in place of the baked or French-fried potato? I prefer it by far to the French-fried onion, but I am of course prejudiced against frying in general. Frying, to my mind, kills the taste of almost everything and would never be missed if we banned it from the twentieth-century kitchen.

Boiled onions with a white wine sauce make an unforgettable dish. Glazed onions with parsley are among the best companions to turkey. Young spring onions are best eaten raw, "natural taste," but they are also wonderful on toast if boiled, minced, and mixed with chopped mushrooms.

Our cookbooks contain very few recipes for onions. In a Spanish cookbook I found and reproduced with great success a dish of sliced onions cooked with milk and a little butter. A Dutch cook once produced for me an onion and potato soup which was superior even to most French onion soups I have eaten.

There are great onion discoveries to make. The onion lends itself to interesting, entertaining, and gratifying experiments, both by itself and in company with other foods whose taste it enhances by its presence.

At the Slim Gourmet's table the onion is restored to the esteem that made Cleopatra offer a dish of onions to Caesar for both culinary and political reasons. The Slim Gourmet cherishes onions for his own good reasons: their taste, and their low count of 60 calories to the cupful.

Talleyrand went to the Vienna Peace Conference to represent defeated France, and returned a victor. The secret of his historic success in diplomacy was his superior knowledge both of the human mind and of the art of eating. "Sire," he wrote to Louis XVIII, "I need casseroles more than written instructions."

Ever since, French diplomacy has considered refined eating an important weapon in the diplomatic arsenal.

A former French ambassador I know cherishes artichokes. An

artichoke is his choice of overture to a meal. In his opinion the French artichoke deserves the highest rank among vegetables, whether it is grown in France, Italy, Belgium, or the United States. When he was on active diplomatic duty, his first activity on arriving in a new country or city was to seek out the supplier of the best artichokes. His next was to teach his cook the best way to prepare and serve them.

His best way was, of course, the simplest, with melted butter. The old gentleman became quite heated in condemnation of his compatriots who eat their artichokes cold with oil and vinegar. Only a modern barbarian, he said, would think of killing with vinegar the earthy, slightly bitter taste of an artichoke that is freshly boiled, well drained, and served not hot but warm, with a little melted butter, sometimes the smallest quantity of a sauce Hollandaise. M. the Ambassador was a man of modest tastes. The best was good enough for him.

That was in 1938, and ever since I have followed the Ambassador's advice. The artichoke has become a favorite at my own table, too, and I have even discovered two additional endearing traits of this divine vegetable.

A medium-sized artichoke is nearly a meal in itself. It contents the appetite. And it counts only 100 calories. Beginning a meal with an artichoke is good strategy for the Slim Gourmet.

Asparagus, my third great table companion, deserves pride of place in this company. May is the month when thousands of crates from California and the Carolinas, Maryland, and Delaware, travel all over the United States, bringing this king of vegetables in season.

In spring asparagus is no longer merely one of two vegetables to be served with the main dish. In spring asparagus *is* the main dish at the table of the Slim Gourmet and the calf's tongue or the ham or the salmon becomes the bridesmaid, the attendant at the asparagus feast.

"Asparagus is a course in its own right," Jean Conil, the London chairman of the Supreme Culinary Council, decreed. He is the man who can serve you asparagus in nineteen different ways. I would add only that my ideal way of honoring this great vegetable is to eat it in May, fresh and without any adornment, simply cooked standing in salted water. Even the Flemish sauce of egg and butter is too much for me during the short time that asparagus is at the peak of its natural taste.

Asparagus is as old as history. The Romans liked it and we still plant it in the same beds and cut it in the same way that the elder Cato described in great detail in his book, *On Farming*, 2,150 years ago.

Nowadays we know four principal varieties:

1.   White asparagus (the best comes from Belgium)
2.   Green asparagus (greatest taste in the United States)
3.   Violet asparagus (from Genoa, Italy)
4.   Canned asparagus (quite a different vegetable from the fresh)

Whenever I see someone eating asparagus as a course in its own right, I sense the presence of a gourmet. It is wrong to classify this gift of nature under the meaningless botanical term "vegetable." One might as accurately call Mr. Bernard Baruch unemployed or Ernest Hemingway a bullfight or safari promoter. Asparagus is in the vegetable world what a Black Angus sirloin steak is among meats, the top of its class, or even in a class by itself.

A main dish of asparagus—twelve or fifteen stalks, cooked just to the point of maintaining their firmness and drained on a white napkin—may be decorated as the occasion warrants with smoked ham or tongue or boiled fresh salmon or breasts of chicken. You eat the stalks with your fingers as did Cato and Fabius Cunctator, who hesitated to give butter to Hannibal but had no hesitation about enjoying his asparagus. A little butter, better fresh than sauced, is all that the Slim Gourmet desires. Spices, herbs, egg sauces, and creamy dressings are not needed to enhance the true taste of fresh asparagus.

The sauces may come to the fore when we eat asparagus out

of season, in the form of the fourth asparagus variety that we can enjoy all year round, thanks to our food industry: canned asparagus. We must, of course, realize that the canning process changes the natural product to some extent. But when we cease to compare the canned vegetable with the taste that fresh asparagus alone can offer, we must acknowledge that asparagus out of a can has a wonderful taste of its own. The taste is so fine that many gourmets all over the world prefer it to inferior fresh asparagus.

Canned asparagus is one of the best friends of the Slim Gourmet. It is preferable to the fresh in salads and all the combinations: mixed vegetables, asparagus soups, omelets, and soufflés. It can, of course, be eaten by itself. At the Slim Gourmet's table canned asparagus, like its fresh brother, is eaten "natural taste" without any taste aid to compete with its flavor.

Asparagus is the Slim Gourmet's friend for its high taste and low calories. The fifteen stalks of a main dish count for no more than 50 calories. If you count another 200 calories for the bridesmaids—the ham, tongue, or salmon—your feast of asparagus in season will cost you no more than 250 calories altogether and give you a quiet conscience with your great taste enjoyment. You are fortunate if you love asparagus as I do and happen to begin your reducing in the month of May.

36 THE SLIM GOURMET ON VACATION

For years my friend Judge O. complained that he gained all his excess weight on his vacations. An ardent huntsman and fisherman, when he spent his month's holiday at a Montana hunting lodge he protested that the all-male company and the long evenings of good talk and good whisky were to blame for his added pounds. In the White Mountains the culprit was the gifted Hungarian cook at his favorite hotel. In Paris it was the wonderful French restaurants—and so on.

Once we made the voyage to Europe together on the *Nieuw Amsterdam* and I saw the weight-gaining marathon with my own eyes. This expert in criminal law, who for eleven months of the year ate like a wise man and a philosopher, took a Dutch breakfast with cheese, herring, ham and eggs; a French luncheon of four courses; an English high tea with muffins and scones; a Southern dinner of ham and roast turkey with all the appurtenances; and the Captain's supper which with its prodigal spread of delicacies looked very Swedish to me, even though we were on a Dutch ship.

His bar bill for the voyage was no more than twenty dollars, but that was because the Dutch put low prices on their tax-free liquor; his calorie bill at the bar ran at least to 12,000. It was no surprise to me that he was six pounds heavier going down the gangplank than when he had ascended it six days before.

"Get-acquainted" binges with new foods in foreign lands need not be so damaging to the waistline. Another friend of mine discovered at the end of a vacation in Italy that he had lost five pounds—without dieting, without knowing quite how he had done it. Fond of spaghetti in all its forms, he had made his journey through Italy a spaghetti tour, sampling *pasta* in every region, prepared in the hundred different ways that only Italians know. Actually he lost weight not in spite of spaghetti but because of it. The many different kinds of *pasta* he enjoyed satisfied not only his appetite but also his taste. His intense enjoyment of each new flavor and texture made him immune to other temptations of the table. Most remarkable, he found he was not tempted to overeat even of spaghetti. His pleasure in new tastes satisfied him so well that he had no need for quantity.

It is unusual to lose weight on a vacation, but it is also unnecessary to gain. The secret of the heavy luncheon in New Orleans or Paris is a very light breakfast; a roll and coffee for *petit déjeuner* content a Frenchman and the Louisianans follow this custom of the city's French founding fathers.

The Dutch eat a mammoth breakfast but hardly any lunch. The Swiss sit from twelve to two o'clock at lunch but have little more than a sandwich at dinner. Vacationing the Slim Gourmet's way does not mean dangerous flirtations with two or three or four countries at once. If we go native, we go a hundred per cent native. We eat the Frenchman's light breakfast as well as his excellent lunch, or the little lunch of the Dutch following their magnificent breakfast. We can eat spaghetti with our Italian hosts if we also eat otherwise as they do—their lean meats and delicate fishes, their abundance of fruits and salad. Nor do we insult their good wine by thoughtlessly downing quarts of it, but enjoy a glass with each meal—and we order only a half-bottle if there are only two of us at table.

But what of the relaxation of our holiday from work? We know that even at home we eat more on week ends than during the working week. How can we enjoy the careless leisure of a vacation and still not suffer the consequences of week-end eating for two or three or four weeks at a stretch?

We save money for a vacation. For some people—myself, for instance—it is also possible to save calories. Just as we eat lightly during the week, when we have less time and need for food, and enjoy our week-end eating without gaining, so we can budget calories for a month or so before vacation and go away lighthearted with enough calories as well as cash to spend.

On vacations, as on week ends, if we eat for taste enjoyment we are not in danger of seriously overeating. The most astonishing display of vacation gluttony I ever witnessed was on the ferry from Sassnitz to Traelleborg on the Baltic Sea. There was a boatload of businessmen and their wives from Leipzig. A handsome *smörgås* was set out in the saloon, and those German burghers and their ladies ate it all, down to the last crumb of delicious Danish cheese. It so happens that in the city in Saxony from which they came, the cooking is probably the poorest in the world—heavy, tasteless, monotonous, combining the worst features of the German cuisine, which can be good but can also be very bad. Those Leipzigers were eating not for present enjoyment but for memory, to be able to tell the stay-at-homes the many rare and sumptuous foods they consumed on their journey. They were also eating to appease the pent-up appetite for good and tasty food that they never could satisfy at home. The pity was that they could no more enjoy their vacation eating than a starving man can enjoy his first meal. It seems to me that eating like a Slim Gourmet the year round, satisfying taste as well as hunger, must protect us from such starvation binges as this.

Some of us use up more calories on vacation than at home. On my own mountain-climbing holidays in Switzerland, for example, I have to eat double the calories I need at work in the city. Hunting, swimming, fishing, golfing, sailing, hiking, bicycling all burn up more calories than sitting at a desk, more even than the efficient housekeeping most women at home do nowadays (but not necessarily more than active gardening or taking care of small children). Tennis every day also requires a different calorie allowance than long lazy days on the beach.

A good rule works both ways. Even if you are reducing, don't succumb to the lure of "doing it once and for all" and set out to lose all your excess weight on vacation. What is a vacation worth that is not pleasure nor recreation nor rest? As we veteran dieters know too well, weight that is too quickly lost is all too quickly regained, and you will have sacrificed your vacation to no purpose after all.

Adjust your maintenance allowance to what you do on vacation: For one hour of brisk walking, add 250 calories to your day's budget; for an hour of rowing, 400 calories; for mountain-climbing, 600.

On vacation in strange places, whether in your own country or abroad, it is a good idea to talk to restaurant captains and waiters about what goes into the dishes you order. A lobster Thermidor, for example, can cost you 400 or 1,200 calories. Vegetables can triple their count with egg, cream, cheese, or other sauces, in resort hotels or foreign restaurants.

For that vacation in Europe, here are a few special Slim Gourmet suggestions:

Go slow on bread in France: a little of this finest bread in the world is delicious, but too much is a sign that you are still tense and need to take some conscious steps toward relaxing.

Eat roast beef and Stilton cheese in England. Many visiting gourmets seek out the French and Italian restaurants in London, but the best of the English cuisine is much better and why should you miss it? Beware, however, of the English addiction to sandwiches.

Order half portions in Holland, Belgium, Switzerland, Denmark, and Sweden, unless you are six feet tall or taller. No waiter will raise an eyebrow. The portions in these countries are designed for giants.

In Italy, eat spaghetti for variety, not quantity. Sample also the *calamari*, which I guarantee you will not recognize as squid; the *scampi*, which you will probably recognize as shrimp, and the mixed salads which combine the greens and vegetables of each season, for instance escarole, cauliflower, tomatoes, kohlrabi, leeks, beetroot or celery root, and boiled potato. Such a salad is a meal in itself and varies from town to town, even from restaurant to restaurant. Papagallo in Bologna makes one of the best, but you must order it in the morning if you want it ready by lunchtime.

Everywhere, order sauces, mayonnaise, and salad dressing served separately. You need no cook to decide how much Hollandaise you want on your cauliflower or Roquefort dressing in your salad. Cooks and waiters often have ancient Roman ideas about these quantities. Remember Lucullus and keep the sauce ladle in your own hands.

Broiling is unknown in Europe. Order your *biftek* or fish dry-grilled.

Avoid table d'hôte dinners; they are always too much to eat. With a little practice you are soon able to order à la carte, eat what you like, as much or as little as you like, and at no greater cost.

When we are in a new land there is a temptation to sample every recommended restaurant, however hastily, with the result that our eating tour is a hodgepodge of specialties not really enjoyed and dangerous to slimness. Another and, to my mind, better way to savor the food of a new place is to choose one good restaurant within one's price class and become a regular customer. In the relaxed mood and with the favored treatment accorded the habitué, aficionado, or stammgast, you can then eat your way at leisure through its menu card, a specialty at a time instead of all at one sitting. Some of the restaurants I like to return to regularly are Giannini in Milan, the Carlton in Brussels, Dikker and Thyss in Amsterdam, Wivex in Copenhagen, and Lapérouse in Paris.

But the first rule is, enjoy taste. You will not need quantity to make your vacation eating a joy unsullied by added pounds.

Book Four

THE SLIM GOURMET'S

FACTS AND FANCIES

37 THE SLIM GOURMET

AT THE DRUGSTORE COUNTER

If American drugstore club sandwiches were sold in France they would get three stars in the tourist guides. I think they are among the better eating treats in the United States. The toasted bread is wonderful, the ingredients are combined for taste, and the average price is very attractive to gourmets, slim or otherwise.

I took one of the world's great gourmets, M. Paul de P. of Lyons, France, to a drugstore counter. I wanted to prove to him that you can have an excellent lunch "the American way." Paul was attracted to the Club Sandwich No. 1 but afraid of its calories. I asked the counter clerk to serve the sandwich with the mayonnaise separate and with knife and fork.

When the sandwich arrived, we took off the top slice of toast and stirred the middle layer with the fork so that the egg and lettuce came in direct contact with the delicious chopped ham salad spiced with chopped cucumbers. Then we ate the whole affair with fork and knife.

The extra mayonnaise we quickly abandoned as superfluous when we discovered how well the chopped ham was already bound with a mayonnaise dressing. This "reduced" club sandwich had only 285 calories instead of the original 585, and was as tasty as the unreduced one. It was just the right luncheon for the Slim Gourmet, who does not want to appear fussy anywhere, even at a drugstore counter.

I hope that one day there will be so many millions of Slim Gourmet followers that all the soda fountaineers will offer special Slim Gourmet sandwiches, omitting superfluous starches and other high-calorie ingredients from their recipes. Until then we shall have to manage in the Slim Gourmet way with what they offer.

Drugstore counters are not out of bounds for reducers. They are dangerous only for thoughtless eaters who do not know what is good, who eat without discrimination, and who have not yet learned what really puts on weight.

The club sandwich I chose is the richest food on most drugstore menus. If even this can be reduced, then the same can be done as easily with other sandwiches. It is second nature to the Slim Gourmet to remove the top of any sandwich and to order, "Mayonnaise separate, please."

The Slim Gourmet at the drugstore counter also:

Eats only half the order of baked beans that comes with frankfurters, eliminating 100 calories; ditto with potato salad.

Drinks his coffee black. Orders iced tea without sugar. Drinks only small glasses of orange juice.

We love what is good to eat and avoid foods that merely fill. Thus at the drugstore counter or anywhere, overweight goes down as surely as the setting sun.

38 TWENTY TASTE TITILLATORS

OF THE SLIM GOURMET

A few drops of good sherry cheer up any consommé. In Greece, years ago, I ate fresh cucumbers with buttermilk, a delectable dish for hot days when we had grown tired of jellied consommé. Any broiled fish is the better for a sprig of fennel. Any fruit salad becomes ambrosial with Grand Marnier and cognac added. Garlic is not so popular as it deserves in the United States, although a good many Americans are discovering that garlic salt confers its unique piquancy on the food only and does not oblige the eater to call for chlorophyll afterward.

The Slim Gourmet's philosophy of natural taste opposes burying the true taste of good food under heavy sauces, but does not object to titillating the palate with a fitting flavor that adds to the enjoyment of the dish.

There are times and situations—on a fisherman's vacation, or during the season for a favorite food—when we like to eat the same food repeatedly. The fisherman, provided he is successful in his fishing, can have trout on Monday "natural taste," on Tuesday broiled in white wine, on Wednesday broiled with fennel.

Boredom in eating is the arch enemy of the Slim Gourmet. Boredom leads to thoughtless overeating. Change and variety are the spice of our eating lives and spice is the tool we use to produce the cheer of variety.

Some years ago I was a guest in a hotel in Jerusalem where eggplant appeared every day on our menu and always prepared the same way.

"This has to happen to me," said a woman doctor from Tel

Aviv, "who taught the housewives of this country more than thirty different ways to prepare eggplant."

"I have read your cookbook and was much impressed," another woman in the company said, "but at this moment I could not quote one of your delightful recipes."

It is a familiar quandary. We study our cookbooks but when the fresh-caught fish or newly picked vegetable is before us we have forgotten what we should do with it or how we should order it prepared. How often have I forgotten, for instance, what a drop of Madeira can do for the onion soup!

While I was reducing, when variety was more than ever essential, I made a little list of twenty taste titillators to be added to different dishes, not to interfere with natural taste but to promote and enhance it. Why twenty, and not fifteen or twenty-five? Because twenty are as many as I could write on a visiting card, to carry in my pocket and consult whenever necessary. For easier remembering I divided my twenty taste titillators into three categories.

First come the sharp ones: mustard, Angostura Bitters, curry powder, kirsch, cognac, applejack.

Next the spicy ones: garlic salt, chives, sherry, paprika, parsley, vermouth, tarragon, fennel.

And finally the light and mild ones: buttermilk, Madeira, Port, Chablis, Grand Marnier, Beaujolais.

This list does not pretend to be complete, merely useful and practical. It changes according to your personal taste, according to your new discoveries in taste titillators. Replace one of the wines on the mild list with beer, for instance. Leave out buttermilk, which you may not like, and put in milk or perhaps ketchup. For Angostura Bitters you may prefer the ready-made English Worcestershire sauce or chili sauce. Whatever you put on your list, remember only that these are *taste titillators*, to be used with a light hand, not to overwhelm but to encourage the good taste of the dish itself.

My twenty taste titillators have served me well and led me

to a great number of taste pleasures. Used with discretion, they not only lead to eating cheer, they are also without exception no calorie wasters. That makes them doubly useful tools for the Slim Gourmet.

39 THE SLIM GOURMET

AND THE TV SNACK

Many people find it necessary to restore their shattered nerves after "Dragnet" or "Foreign Intrigue" or the fight or the ball game with 300 calories of peanuts or 150 calories of beer. "What can I do?" pleaded my friend Fred. "There I sit with all my hopes, expectations, and bets—and there's the home run. I have to let off steam or explode."

Of course the peanuts are within easy reach and the beer is two steps away in the kitchen refrigerator. These unplanned nerve medicines destroy the best-planned food balance. What shall we do? Not eat the peanuts? Not drink the beer?

"Don't tell me I should eat carrot sticks," our weight-gaining superintendent told me. "You can make me eat them between lunch and dinner, but for TV I want a glass of Irish whisky or some of the wine mother used to make." (122 calories for the Irish and 160 calories for mother's wine.)

Fred can have his beer, Jim has wine or whisky, but they can also do a little prior planning as their wives plan the family budget. If TV snacks are essential, the Slim Gourmet provides for them. Here are a few safe rules for feeding TV nerves:

Prepare cool low-calorie drinks when it is hot. Sucarylsweetened lemonade is popular. Iced tea is welcomed. Grapefruit juice with soda needs no sweetening.

Coke, mother's wine, beer, and many other drinks taste even better when sipped instead of gulped. Drink coke "on the rocks," beer out of wine glasses. Drink wine in a two and one-half ounce glass.

Replace nuts, chocolates, potato chips, by hard candy. Have pineapple cubes on toothpicks. Prepare an iced bowl of fruit salad.

It doesn't matter to your TV appetite *what* you eat, only that you eat something. The Slim Gourmet way is to reserve 150-250 calories of the daily budget for TV evenings. If you don't need that much, no harm is done.

But if TV snacks add only 200 unbudgeted calories at each of the 150 TV evenings the average family enjoys in a year, that's nine pounds gained as sure as Groucho smokes cigars.

40   SOME REDUCING FRIENDS

OF THE SLIM GOURMET

The most gregarious person likes some people better than others. He sees some of his friends more frequently and there are a few with whom he enjoys daily meetings for years.

It is only natural that even the Slim Gourmet with the widest food acquaintance has some special friends. We like to change our menus. We know many dishes. We make taste excursions. But in our eating as in our social life or our choice of hats or ties, we all develop an affection for a few favorites.

I found it especially important to associate with the right

food friends during my reducing period, when I was living on fewer calories than I could normally afford. To make the choice of the right friends easier, I composed a list of reducing friends —foods that can be eaten in fairly generous quantities without adding too many calories to our menus. There were enough candidates for such friendships on my list so that I could be quite choosey and select only those I really liked.

Turnips, for instance, are calorie-kind to reducers, and I am fond of turnips. But you need not eat turnips if you don't enjoy them. I give you my list but with a pencil and a little time you can make it your own by adding candidates for your reducing friendship that will please your palate.

During the time of my reducing I carried this list in my pocket notebook, to consult for ideas when I bought or ordered food. A generous serving of any of these is not more than 50 calories, and some, as you can see, are even less:

ABOUT 25 CALORIES

asparagus	broccoli	cabbage
cauliflower	canned carrots	celery
cucumbers	endive	lettuce
radishes	sauerkraut	spinach
tomatoes	rhubarb	

NOT MORE THAN 35 CALORIES

eggplant	kohlrabi	leeks
okra	parsley	peppers
pumpkins	turnips	blackberries
melons	strawberries	

NOT MORE THAN 50 CALORIES

Brussels sprouts	peaches
fresh onions	limes
water-canned apricots	tangerines
grapefruit	fresh carrots
lemons	unsweetened apple sauce
raspberries	blueberries
beets	pears
peas	oranges

41 A WEEK'S REDUCING MENUS

OF THE SLIM GOURMET

In my notebook I have a record of what I ate each day of the seventy-eight weeks during which I reduced. It is a very personal record. It reveals how one individual, who loved food and took great pleasure in eating, lost eighty-two pounds in that time but lost not one moment of his joy in eating. As I write this, the record is already more than a year old. I weigh not one ounce more than I did when I came to the last day of the seventy-eighth and final week of my reducing program. I enjoy eating more than ever. I do not have even a secret desire to eat more or differently.

Eating is personal. So is reducing. Menus while reducing should therefore NOT be read as a diet. They are an example of one man's application of the Slim Gourmet's philosophy, given here only to show how attractive eating can be even while reducing on a weekly allowance of 12,600 calories or 1,800 calories a day.

These menus look quite different from the diets that promise miracles. They were in fact quite different, because seventy-eight weeks of eating like this and better lightened me by one pound a week even while I enjoyed every day and every meal.

My eating ideas may be very different from yours, but you will not criticize my choices because they are not your own, as I will never reject your taste because it differs from mine. Beginning at the same point on our Slim Gourmet way, you and I will go by quite different routes, but we will come at the end of our journey to the same happy haven, our normal weight and a way of joyful eating that will content us and keep us from ever having to make the journey back from overweight again.

First, for curiosity's sake, here is a typical day's eating out of my life before I began to reduce the Slim Gourmet's way. (I had, as you know, reduced in seventeen other ways before, and was thoroughly discouraged from trying again.)

I made no notes on my eating before the Slim Gourmet was born. This is a sample found by chance in one of my notebooks, from the time when I was taking inventory of my food habits and trying to discover why I could not keep my normal weight:

Breakfast:	coffee with cream or sugar—70 calories
	ham and eggs—300 calories
	2 slices bread—140 calories
	1 apple—100 calories
Lunch:	1 tongue and cheese sandwich—400 calories
	1 frankfurter sandwich—300 calories
	coffee with cream and sugar—70 calories
Dinner:	1 whisky with soda—100 calories
	thick pea soup—200 calories
	2 breaded veal cutlets with mashed potatoes—400 calories
	lemon meringue pie—500 calories
Snacks:	1 cognac—100 calories
	1 thick piece of salami—200 calories
	1 cracker—50 calories

TOTAL—2,930 calories

This was not an exceptional day and it was not even a day when I enjoyed great cooking and gourmet eating. It was a typical weekday downtown when I was characteristically "too busy" to devote any attention to the choice of my eating. On this quite ordinary day, however, I overate to the tune of 500 calories. If I had done so every day I would have gained a pound a week.

Four meals, then as now, are my regular program. I go to bed late and cannot be happy with nothing to eat from dinner until midnight. My food habit inventory revealed that I would encounter no great difficulties in making my breakfast and especially my luncheon lighter, but that I would have to have a substantial dinner and could not go without the after-dinner snack.

One week's eating during my reducing interval shows what ways I changed and how I changed them.

A real and factual eating report is bound to be different from an "ideal eating program." However we live, we don't live under ideal laboratory conditions and therefore we can rarely eat under ideal conditions.

My eating report is therefore the result of quite a number of compromises with those who made menus for me and with situations in which I could not act entirely on my principles. If one reads it, however, with the understanding that man is a social animal, it is fairly good evidence that reducing does not succeed only in seclusion, but can be undertaken unobtrusively and pleasantly without disturbing our personal and social lives.

There were days when at one or two meals at least I could decide what I was going to eat, entirely on my own. The 400-calorie luncheon with Bulgarian Salad was made possible by the cooperation of a friendly waiter. A friend of mine had discovered that Bulgarians believe Yoghurt to be the reason why so many of their countrymen live to be a hundred. He argued that Yoghurt could never be a popular dish, and for answer I invited him and a few others to participate in a Bulgarian "Springtime Yoghurt" such as I had once eaten at the house of a Bulgarian businessman in Paris. We all enjoyed it, my friend conceded the argument, and the restaurant listed the luncheon for a few weeks afterward on its regular menu.

Another meal which I was able to compose to suit myself was breakfast. For me a different breakfast every day includes a different hot drink, to do away with the bad custom of forgetting what one is drinking, just so it is hot.

The eating report illustrates also how very personal the allocation of the week's calories must be for each day of the week. For me the last three days of the week are punctuated with social engagements, visits, and family parties.

Reading this list again, I see that it is rather dry. "1 glass of wine—70 calories" gives no idea of the 1947 Clos Vougeot that was served, with its unforgettable perfume of overripe raspberries. I sat over this one glass of wine for more than an hour and even left the cranberry sauce on my plate so as not to miss any part of the Burgundy's great taste. The "omelet with shrimps" was not just a simple omelet. It was made by a master of the art of omelet creation. It was beautiful to look at in its bright yellow color, and a soft dough enveloped the shrimps, which were piquant with the chopped parsley they had been dipped in beforehand.

No list can reproduce the savor and flavor of all the foods it comprises. But though the list is a pale reflection of the original experiences, it reveals how the joy of eating can make reducing, too, a joy.

This was my eating from May 4 to May 10, 1953. My reducing allowance for the week was 12,600 calories.

THIS IS MY EATING FROM MAY 4 TO MAY 10, 1953

WEEKLY REDUCING CALORIE ALLOWANCE—12,600

BREAKFAST	CAL.	LUNCHEON	CAL.	DINNER	CAL.	AFTER DINNER	CAL.	TOTAL CALORIES
Monday, 5/4/53								
China tea	0	½ glass milk	85	California fresh asparagus natural taste with smoked calf's tongue	250	1 glass red wine	70	
1 slice toast with butter	70	½ cold lobster "natural taste"	100			1 wedge Camembert	110	
Fruit salad	50	Green tossed salad with 2 egg whites and pearl onion dressing	100	Cantaloupe with bourbon	100	1 slice pumpernickel	80	
grapefruit cherries	70	1 roll	80	Coffee with cream, sugar	70			
				Almond coffee cake	200			
	190		365		620		260	1435
Tuesday, 5/5/53								
Coffee with cream, sugar	70	Bulgarian salad	180	Shrimp cocktail in cream and port wine sauce	150	½ glass orange juice	75	
½ glass prune juice	125	Yoghurt Cucumbers	30	Onion soufflé	200	1 slice liver sausage	75	
2 soft-poached eggs	140	Spring onions	50	1 slice old cheddar cheese	120	1 slice toast	70	
		Tomatoes	50					
		Spices	10					

1 slice dry bread 70	1 roll 80	1 slice rye bread 100	
	1 cup black coffee 0	1 cup Darjeeling tea 0	
405	400	570	1595
			220

Wednesday, 5/6/53

1 glass filtered black coffee 0	1 McIntosh apple with sprinkled brandy 125	1 cold Madrilène 25	1 large glass wine with water 70
1½ eggs "Slim Gourmet":	Chopped sirloin steak with asparagus salad 320	Sweetbreads braised with capers 200	Nuts and almonds 200
½ hard-boiled egg with red caviar 45	1 roll 80	1 baked potato 100	
½ hard-boiled egg with chopped olives 40	Turkish coffee with sugar 40	1 glass claret 75	
½ deviled egg with cottage cheese and red horseradish 50		1 slice Swiss cheese, cracker 150	
1 slice toast 70			
½ pat butter 30			
235	565	550	270
			1620

THIS IS MY EATING FROM MAY 4 TO MAY 10, 1953 (Continued)

WEEKLY REDUCING CALORIE ALLOWANCE—12,600 (Continued)

BREAKFAST	CAL.	LUNCHEON	CAL.	DINNER	CAL.	AFTER DINNER	CAL.	TOTAL CALORIES
Thursday, 5/7/53								
Earl Grey tea	0	Tomato juice	50	½ grapefruit, hot with little Kirsch	75	Roast beef sandwich	375	
1 slice toast with butter	70	Omelet with shrimp and green peas	300	Calves' liver with spinach "natural taste"	200	Beer in wine glass	55	
	50	1 cup coffee with cream, sugar	70	Soufflé with Grand Marnier	250			
1 Winesap apple	100			1 glass white wine	70			
				Black coffee	0			
	220		420		595		430	1665
Friday, 5/8/53								
Cup black coffee	0	Chef's salad (in restaurant)	150	Dinner Party:		2 whiskies	200	
Grapefruit juice	50	1 American Camembert	110	Artichoke, "natural taste"	70	Fruit salad with Cointreau	150	
Bran Flakes with milk	150	1 roll	80	Turkey with all trimmings	400	1 Cola	100	
1 soft-boiled egg	70	1 cup black coffee	0	Cheese cake (small portion)	150			
				1 glass wine	70			
	270		340		690		450	1750

Saturday, 5/9/53

Lapsang Souchong tea	0	Porterhouse steak (small portion)	350	Chicken consommé with noodles	75	2 whiskies	200
Orange juice	100	1 baked potato	100	Veal cutlet stuffed with Parmesan cheese	450	6 cheese crackers	150
Ham and eggs	300	Roquefort cheese	100	Asparagus	50	1 glass buttermilk	80
1 slice toast	70	Butter and	30	Fresh strawberries	50		
with butter	50	Cracker	50	Black coffee	0		
		Coffee with cream and sugar	70				
	520		700		625		430

2275

Sunday, 5/10/53

Tomato juice	50	Spaghetti with 2 pats butter and shredded green olives and diced frankfurters	400	Asparagus soup	100	2 cups coffee cream and sugar	140
Black coffee	0	Fresh fruit salad "natural taste"	150	Saddle of lamb with mustard and red wine sauce	400	Pineapple cheese cake	300
Chicken liver omelet	300			Broccoli "natural taste"	50		
2 slices French bread	140			Rhubarb with strawberries	100		
Butter	50						
Jam	50						
	590		550		650		440

Total for the week   12,570

42 WHAT 100 CALORIES WILL BUY

The following table, which I elaborated for my own reducing, has proven to be easy to use. The calorie-values are mainly based on "Food Values in Common Portions," a publication of the U.S. Department of Agriculture. The portions have been tried out for more than two years and, while approximate and in round numbers, are exact enough for the Slim Gourmet's purpose.

100-CALORIE GUIDE

FOOD	PORTION	WEIGHT (OZ.)	FOOD	PORTION	WEIGHT (OZ.)
Almonds	10	0.6	Blueberry pie	1/12 pie	1.5
Anchovies	13 fillets	2.0	Bluefish	1 piece	3.0
Apple, fresh	1 large	6.0	Bologna sausage	2 thin sl.	1.6
Apple juice	¾ cup	6.0	Bourbon	1 pony	0.7
Apple pie	1/12 part	2.0	Bouillon	3 cups	24.0
Apple sauce	½ cup	4.0	Bran, wheat	1 cup	2.0
Apricots, fresh	5	6.0	Brandy	1 pony	0.7
Apricot juice	⅔ cup	7.0	Brazil nuts	2 nuts	0.5
Artichoke	1 large	6.0	Bread	1¼ slice	1.4
Asparagus, fresh	20-30 stalks	15.0	Brie cheese	1 sm. wedge	1.5
canned	2 cups	13.0	Broccoli	3 stalks	10.0
Avocado	¼ fruit	1.6	Brussels sprouts	12 sprouts	6.0
Bacon, broiled	2-3 slices	0.6	Butter	2 sm. squares	0.5
medium uncooked	1½ sl.	0.6	Butterfish	1 piece	2.0
Bananas, fresh	1 banana	3.5	Buttermilk	1 cup	8.0
Bass	1 slice	4.0	Cabbage, fresh	3 cups	12.0
Beans,			Cake, Angel	1 slice	1.3
baked with pork	⅓ cup	3.0	fruit	1 sm. slice	1.0
lima	½ cup	3.0	sponge	1 sm. slice	1.0
string	2 cups	9.0	Camembert cheese	1 wedge	1.0
Beef, broth	3 cups	24.0	Cantaloupe	½ mellon	15.0
corned	1 slice	1.0	Carrots, fresh	5-6 carrots	8.0
loin	1 slice	1.5	Cauliflower	1 head	12.0
rib	1 slice	1.3	Caviar	5 tbs.	1.3
sirloin steak	1 sm. slice	2.0	Celery	4 cups	18.0
Beer	½ can	6.0	Cheese, American	sm. cube	1.0
Beets, fresh	4 beets	8.0	Cheese sandwich	⅓ sand.	4.0
Blackberries, fresh	40 berries	6.0	Cheese soufflé	½ cup	2.0
Blueberries, fresh	1 cup	5.0	Cherries, fresh	1 cup	6.0

100-CALORIE GUIDE *(Continued)*

FOOD	PORTION	WEIGHT (OZ.)	FOOD	PORTION	WEIGHT (OZ.)
canned	½ cup	4.0	yolk only	2 yolks	1.0
Chestnuts	8	2.0	Figs, fresh	3 small	4.0
Chicken, broiled	½ chicken	4.0	dried	2 small	1.2
roast	⅓ chicken	3.0	Flounder	1 slice	6.0
Chocolate, sweet	sm. piece	0.5	Frankfurter	1 sausage	1.5
Chow Mein	½ cup	4.0	French Dressing	1½ tbs.	0.5
Cider	¾ cup	6.0	Frogs' legs	2-3 legs	5.0
Clams	6 clams	5.0	Fruit salad	1 cup	8.0
Club sandwich	¼ sand.		Gefuelte fish	½ cup	4.0
Cocktails	½ portion	2.0	Gin	1½ pony	1.0
Cocoa	⅓ cup	3.0	Ginger, candied	6 pieces	1.0
Codfish	1 slice	5.0	Goose	small slice	2.0
Coffee, black	(no caloric value)		Gooseberries	2 cups	8.0
Cola drinks	1 full glass	8.0	Grapefruit, fresh	½ fruit	8.0
Consommé	3 cups	24.0	juice	1 cup	8.0
Cookies,			Grape juice	½ cup	4.0
Lady fingers	3	1.0	Grapes	1 lg. bunch	5.0
Oatmeal-raisin	1	1.5	Griddle cake	1 cake	2.0
Corn, canned	½ cup	4.0	Gumdrops	3 pieces	2.0
flakes	1¼ cup	1.0	Haddock	good portion	5.0
Corned beef			Halibut	small piece	3.0
sandwich	⅓ sand.		Ham, fresh, lean	good slice	1.5
Crabs, fresh	½ cup	4.5	Hamburger	very sm. pat.	3.0
canned meat	½ cup	4.0	Hash, corned beef	⅓ cup	2.5
Crackers,			Hazelnuts	9 nuts	0.5
cheese or oyster	20 crackers	1.0	Herring	⅓ herring	3.0
normal size	3 crackers	1.0	Hickory nuts	12 nuts	0.5
saltines	6 crackers	1.0	Honeydew melon	2 cups	10.0
Cranberries, fresh	1¾ cup	7.0	Horse radish	20 tbs.	10.0
sauce	¼ cup	1.5	Ice cream	⅓ scoop	2.0
Cream, medium	¼ cup	1.5	Ice cream soda	⅓ glass	2.0
whipped	3 tbs.	1.0	Jam—marmalade—		
Cream cheese	2 tbs.	1.0	jellies	1½ tbs.	1.5
Cucumbers	3 whole cuc.	24.0	Kale	1½ cups	8.0
Custard	1 cust'd cup	4.0	Kidney, veal	1 kidney	3.0
Custard pie	1/12 pie	2.0	beef	½ kidney	2.6
Dates	4 dates	1.0	Kohlrabi	2 cups	10.0
Doughnuts	½ d-nut	1.0	Kumquats	7 fruits	5.0
Duck	½ breast		Lamb, chops	1 rib chop	2.0
	or 1 thigh	2.2	leg or shoulder	1 sm. slice	2.0
Eggs,	1⅓ eggs	2.0	Leeks	7 leeks	8.0
whites only	7 whites	7.5	Lemon, juice	1 lg. glass	8.0

100-CALORIE GUIDE *(Continued)*

FOOD	PORTION	WEIGHT (OZ.)	FOOD	PORTION	WEIGHT (OZ.)
pie	1/12 part	1.0	Oxtail soup	½ plate	4.0
Lemons	3 lg. fruit	7.5	Oysters	5 medium	4.0
Lentils, dried	2 tbs.	1.0	Parsnips	1 parsnip	4.0
Lettuce	2 lg. heads	20.0	Pastrami	½ thin sl.	1.0
Liederkranz cheese	2 tbs.	1.0	Pâté de foie gras	½ tb.	1.0
Liver	1 good slice	2.5	Peaches, fresh	2 medium	7.0
Liverwurst	1 slice	1.5	canned	2 lg. halves	3.0
Lobster, fresh	⅔ cup	4.0	Peach pie	1/12 pie	2.0
Macaroni, uncooked	¼ cup	1.0	Peanuts, roasted	20 peanuts	0.5
Macaroons	2 macaroons	1.0	Pears, fresh	1 large	5.0
Manhattan cocktail	½ glass	1.5	canned	4 halves	4.0
Marshmallows	5 marshmall.	1.0	Peas, fresh green	¾ cup	3.5
Martini, dry	1 sm. glass	2.0	canned	¾ cup	6.0
Mayonnaise	1 tb.	0.5	dried split	2 tbs.	1.0
Milk, skimmed	1¼ cup	10.0	Pea soup	½ plate	4.0
whole	½ cup	4.0	Peppers, green	5 peppers	12.0
Mince pie	1/16 pie	1.0	Pheasant	1 good sl.	2.5
Mints, cream	10 small	0.5	Pickles, sour	10	10.0
chocolate	1 large	0.2	sweet	5	4.0
Muffins	1 muffin	2.0	Pineapple,		
Mushrooms	10 mushrooms	4.0	canned or fresh	2 slices	6.0
Mushroom soup	½ plate	4.0	juice	⅔ cup	6.0
Mussels	8 mussels	4.0	Plums,		
Mustard	5 tbs.	3.0	canned or fresh	4 fruits	6.5
Mutton chops	½ chop	2.0	Pompano	1 slice	2.5
Nectarines	3 fruits	6.0	Pork, chops	½ lean chp.	2.0
Nectarine juice	⅔ glass	6.0	tenderloin	½ slice	2.5
Noodles, uncooked	¼ cup	1.0	Potato, boiled	1 medium	4.0
Noodle soup	1 cup	8.0	mashed	½ cup	3.5
Nougats	2 pieces	1.0	chips	8 lg. pcs.	0.5
Oatmeal, cooked	¾ cup	5.0	salad	¼ cup	2.0
Oil	1 tb.	0.4	soup	½ cup	4.0
Okra	25 pieces	9.0	Pretzels	2 large or	
Old-fashioned	⅓ glass	1.0		12 small	1.0
Olives, green	11 olives	3.0	Prune, juice	½ cup	4.0
ripe	8 olives	2.0	whip	½ cup	2.5
Omelet	1 egg	2.5	dried or fresh	4 medium	1.5
Onions	¾ medium	7.0	Pumpkin, fresh	large piece	10.0
Onion soup	⅔ plate	6.0	pie	1/12 pie	2.0
Oranges	1 large	7.0	Radishes	40 small	15.0
Orange, juice	⅔ cup	6.0	Raisins	2 tbs.	1.0
marmalade	1 tb.	1.0	Raspberries	1 cup	5.0

100-CALORIE GUIDE *(Continued)*

FOOD	PORTION	WEIGHT (OZ.)	FOOD	PORTION	WEIGHT (OZ.)
Raspberry juice	1¼ cup	10.0	Strawberries,		
Red wine (dry)	1½ glass	5.0	fresh or canned	1¼ cups	9.0
Rhine wine	1½ glass	5.0	Sturgeon	good slice	4.0
Rhubarb, raw	4 cups	20.0	Sugar, cubes	4 lumps	
stewed	½ cup	4.0	powdered	2½ tbs.	
pie	1/12 pie	1.5	Sweetbreads, calf	⅓ pair	3.0
Rice, cooked	¾ cup	4.0	Sweet potatoes	½ potato	3.0
Rice Krispies	¾ cup	1.0	Swordfish	½ slice	3.0
Roast beef	1 slice	2.0	Tangerines	2 medium	7.0
Roe, shad, carp,			Tangerine juice	½ glass	4.0
salmon, cod	⅓ medium	2.5	Terrapin	1 avg. serv.	3.0
Rolls	1 medium	1.2	Tomatoes, fresh	3 tomatoes	
Roquefort cheese	sm. wedge	1.0	juice	2 cups	16.0
Roquefort dressing	1 tb.	1.0	soup	½ cup	4.0
Rum (Cuban)	1½ pony	1.0	ketchup	2 tbs.	1.0
Rye bread	1 slice	2.0	Tongue, beef	2 slices	1.5
Rye whisky	1 pony	0.7	Triscuit	4 wafers	0.8
Salami	⅔ slice	0.8	Trout	½ medium	3.0
Salmon,			Tuna fish, canned	¼ cup	1.5
fresh or canned	½ cup	2.0	Turkey	1 slice	2.0
smoked	1 slice	2.0	Turnip, greens	½ cup	3.0
Sardines, canned	5 sardines	2.0	white	4 turnips	10.0
Sauerkraut	3½ cups	17.0	Turtle	average port.	4.0
Scallops	⅔ cup	5.0	Veal, breast	½ slice	2.0
Scotch whisky	1½ pony	1.0	steak	⅓ steak	2.5
Shad	1 good slice	2.0	cutlet	⅓ cutlet	2.2
Sherbets	½ scoop	2.0	Vegetable soup	½ plate	4.0
Shrimps	5 large	4.0	Waffles	1 waffle	2.0
Sirup, maple	1½ tbs.	1.0	Walnuts	10 halves	1.0
Smelts	2 small	4.0	Watercress	4 bunches	16.0
Soy sauce	1 cup	6.0	Watermelon	medium sl.	12.0
Spaghetti, cooked	½ cup	4.0	Wheat bread	1⅓ sl.	1.0
Spinach	2 cups	16.0	Whisky	1½ pony	1.0
Split pea soup	⅔ cup	6.0	Whitefish	⅓ port.	3.0
Squab	½ bird	1.5	White wine (dry)	1½ glass	5.0
Squash, fresh	½ squash	12.0	Yoghurt	⅔ cup	6.0
			Zwieback	3 pieces	1.0

A NOTE ABOUT THE AUTHOR

MARTIN LEDERMAN, *by profession a management consultant and by preference a world traveler and gourmet, is also noted as an authority on the joys of eating and the realities of weight reduction. He believes that eating is a life-enhancing pastime.*

He developed this into a fine art after more than thirty years of systematic study in Europe, the Middle East, and in the United States. Mr. Lederman's concept of the Slim Gourmet was developed during the past five years. He worked it out when he changed his own rather considerable weight of 250 pounds to his present weight of 168 pounds, to which he has steadily kept for more than two years.

Mr. Lederman is married and lives in New York City. His book on the Slim Gourmet was written after fifteen thousand letter writers from all over America had asked him more questions on eating than he could answer individually.